Why Can't I Make People Understand?

Discovering the validat... . those with chronic illness seek and why

Conquering the Confusions
of Chronic Illness Series

Lisa J. Copen

[RMP]

Rest Ministries Publishers
SAN DIEGO, CA

Why Can't I Make People Understand?
Discovering the validation those with chronic illness seek and why
Conquering the Confusions of Chronic Illness Series
Copyright © 2005, 2007, 2012 by Lisa J. Copen
Cover Design © 2004, JLC Productions

ISBN: 978-0-9716600-4-2
Library of Congress Control Number: 2004094511

Request for information should be sent to:
Rest Ministries, Inc., a Christian organization
that serves people who live with chronic illness or pain.
P.O. Box 502928, San Diego, CA 92150
858-486-4685; Toll-free 888-751-REST (7378)
Web site: restministries.com; Email: rest@restministries.org

Printed in the United States of America

Dedicated to

*All of you who live with
chronic illness who make it possible
for me to feel like someone understands.*

*And to my husband, Joel, and my family,
who have done everything
they possibly can to understand.*

*"Rejoice in the Lord always. I
will say it again: Rejoice! Let your gentleness be
evident to all. The Lord is near. Do not be anxious
about anything, but in everything, by prayer and
petition, with thanksgiving, present your requests to
God. And the peace of God, which transcends all
understanding, will guard your hearts and
your minds in Christ Jesus."
Philippians 4:4–7*

CONTENTS

INTRODUCTION
Why do I need people to understand me?

"Oh, you look so good! You must be feeling a lot better."

It's a kind word of encouragement and yet we've all felt the twinge of "if you only knew" that sparks possible heartache or resentment. *They don't have a clue how poorly I feel. It took everything to get up today and brush my hair. Little do they know!* Emotions well up within our hearts as we contemplate whether to smile and say, "Thank you" or jump into our lament of "Well, I feel a lot worse than I look. . . ."

"You look great!" is just simple praise, but curiously it brings frustration and discouragement to the majority of people with chronic illness. Rather than glowing words of admiration we hear, "You must not really be that bad," or "Your illness obviously isn't serious, because you look like you've recovered fine. I don't know why you're making such a big deal out of this."

If you have picked up this book, it's probably because you or someone you know lives with the challenge of chronic illness. Living with a chronic condition is far from fun, but it is possible—over 105 million people in the United States prove they can function on some level, even when their bodies don't function 100 percent effectively. We adapt to our changes, we learn how to navigate the maze of the medical system, and God's presence may feel closer than ever before. So why, when someone makes a sincere but ignorant comment about our health, do we feel like screaming and slamming doors? Why do we feel a flash of guilt and an impending confrontation as soon as we pull into a disabled parking space? Although we understand the battle of illness, we grow weary at the daily-ness of side effects, financial struggles, and our deteriorating body; when someone offers their opinion on our coping skills, we quickly become angry and disheartened about the lack of understanding from those around us.

> "I have thin hair and wear a lot of hats," shares Joyce, who lives with lupus. "An older lady at my church said, 'Why don't you buy some hair? After all, if you didn't have teeth you would buy some. The Bible says, "A woman's hair is her glory."' Like I wouldn't choose to have hair!"

Perhaps you're beginning to uncover God's blessings and lessons in the pain and even weathering the stormy challenges with a positive attitude. But then reality hits. *What? You mean it's forever? I know I said I'd learn a lesson, Lord, but I prefer the Cliff-notes version!*

Wishing People Could Just "Get It"

> "I just couldn't believe she told me that I didn't earn a vacation since I didn't have to work," shared Casey. "I know I look like I'm healthy, but it's not as if I'm out running around a track or anything. Everyone always seems to think I am just a little housewife who does nothing all day but sit around and watch soaps. If they only knew how much I'd love to be working and how much I miss my job. It feels like the whole world is out to misunderstand everything about me. I don't know how to get them to see the truth."

We want people to realize how dramatically our lives have been interrupted. Even Jesus, while teaching a lesson to His disciples, became frustrated when they just weren't "getting it." He rebuked them by saying, "Are you so dull?" (Mark 7:18). Although I wouldn't recommend quoting Jesus on this one and calling your response "scriptural," it's reassuring to know that the human side of Him felt our impatience with others' lack of ability to recognize our meaning.

In the midst of wanting to throw the covers over our heads we suddenly feel backed into a corner and forced to defend the mere existence of our illness to others. Dr. Carrie Carter, author of *Thrive: A Woman's Guide to a Healthy Lifestyle*, lives with Meniere's disease. "There's something in me," shares Dr. Carter, "that rises up and wants to say, 'but I'm still sick! I really am!' I want people to understand that, and yet it shouldn't matter what people think. . . . But it does. It's that in-between place that is very weird."[1]

> *"In the end, we will remember not the words of our enemies but the silence of our friends."*
> —*Martin Luther King Jr.*

We hope for a miracle healing, but frankly, we're too busy trying to make life-altering decisions about medications and treatments to spend all of our emotional energy praying for that healing. We do pray; we lift up our requests, and all we get back in return is silence. We start taking the medications, and we learn to accept the prick of a needle without passing out. *Okay, Lord, if this is what You want, I surrender it over to You. I have no control. Just promise You'll never leave my side. And, oh, Lord, I could really use a friend right now.*

Then your friends begin to call. . .and they wonder why you've given up on God so fast. "I can't believe you're giving in to this illness! Jesus died on the cross to protect you from the sin of this world. You have to name it and claim it!" "Have you asked God to forgive all your sins?

There must be something you're forgetting."

> "Everyone who meets me wants to put their hands on me for God's healing," says Susan, who has Tardive Dyskinesia, a neurological syndrome. "They just seem to assume it's okay."

Proverbs 19:2 says, "It is not good to have zeal without knowledge, nor to be hasty and miss the way." While those who love us may have zeal—they have passion to see us well and receive God's best—they may not have the knowledge of how to approach us or how to deal with their own emotions when they see us in so much pain. By understanding this, we can save ourselves much heartbreak.

> "I'll never forget the first time I saw my brother after I was diagnosed with scleroderma," shares Shannon. "It had been two years since we'd been together, and when he picked me up at the airport, he gave me a hug and said, 'Well, you don't feel stiff to me at all. I think you made this organ-hardening thing up just to get some attention.' He was just teasing, but it stung so deeply. He has no idea about the kind of fears I live with each day, and in less than ten seconds it felt like he was making fun of every one of them."

Good Intentions but Bad Outcome

Most people around us care a great deal about our well-being, and when they make these comments we try our hardest to rise above the hurt feelings and recognize the concern in their hearts. Sometimes, the "wounds from a friend can be trusted" (Proverbs 27:6), because the remarks are made out of ignorance. They are grasping to say anything that can communicate their love—it just comes out all wrong.

When I was diagnosed with rheumatoid arthritis, those at my church and work felt no reluctance in holding back their opinions. As a twenty-four-year-old young woman, a thousand miles away from my family, the decisions I was forced into making about treatment options felt overwhelming and serious. I took great care in researching therapies, consulting doctors, and comparing the immediate side effects of medications with the long-term results of not taking the drugs. The scattered advice from people who knew nothing about my illness felt like a personal attack against my intellect. The audacity of those who casually made ignorant statements about my faith, however, hurt even more. Have you had a friend who "finds no pleasure in understanding but delights in airing his own opinions" (Proverbs 18:2)?

At the beginning of my illness, seeking wisdom from those who had traveled this path before me, I read the inspirational autobiographies of Joni Eareckson Tada and Dave Dravecky. They have been on the receiving end of similar comments and even insults; I grasped onto the assurance that God was the only One who knew my heart. If strangers were willing to tell these heroes in the suffering ministry that they lacked the faith to be healed, what made me think I was exempt from criticisms and skepticism? If you are wondering if something is wrong with you because people suggest you lack faith, guess what? You are not alone.

Through Rest Ministries, the Christian organization I began in 1997 for people who live with chronic illness, I have the honor of speaking and exhibiting to large audiences. Each time, however, I am vulnerable to hearing, "If you had enough faith you would be healed." Many times, people glance over the display table and exclaim, "This is wonderful, but you could try [fill in the blank], and then God would heal you, and then *that* could be your ministry!" I've also heard some rather derogatory remarks, and it's never easy to smile and say, "I appreciate your concern, but I don't agree."

Personally, I don't have a passion for a healing ministry, but rather for one that reaches out to people during their illness and walks alongside them. If this means that I will have to walk the walk (or someday wheel?), then I will do so, because I consider it pure joy to suffer for Christ (1 Peter 4:13).

But...oh! I hate pain! And during many moments I am *not* considering it pure joy at all! I dislike suffering just as much as you, and I *do* know pain. Walking, standing, sleeping, typing, and generally just moving are all daily challenges for me. Most days I awake and wonder *how* severe the pain will be that day, not *if* it will be a painful day. X-rays of joints show what the doctors describe as "severe erosion." Only with God's strength am I able to make it through each day.

> *"Never, never pin your whole faith on any human being: not if he is the best and wisest in the whole world. There are lots of nice things you can do with sand; but do not try building a house on it."*
> —C. S. Lewis

God gives us grace and endurance, just as He gave the Israelites manna—as much as we need for the moment. Like the Israelites, I also want to be a bit whiny and to say, *L-o-o-o-r-d, I'm tired of the manna!* But God is less concerned about our earthly comforts than He is our eternal souls.

Where Does My Longing Come From?

We have a great yearning to feel needed and assured that we make a difference. We want R-E-S-P-E-C-T. Is this sin?

According to Larry Crabb, author of *Inside Out,* we need to acknowledge that we have desires. The fact that we long to matter is due to two reasons: Reason #1: In God's wisdom and kindness we were designed with free will; Reason #2: Because sin introduced us to separation between God and us. [2]

Crabb explains that God designed us to want to feel needed and valued, but when Adam and Eve sinned, we were separated from God, never able to have that utopian Garden of Eden feeling here on earth. Jesus came and gave us new hope through eternal salvation, but we're designed to wish for something that ultimately cannot be given to us here on earth—complete and utter fulfillment. Crabb also says that if we'd never sinned, we'd have lived with a realization of our part in God's work, rather than a desperate desire to find meaning. So, wanting to feel respected is only natural because it's the way God made us; not ever feeling it 100 percent here on earth is because of the sin of man.

If It's So Natural Then Why Do I Need to Deny It?

According to Romans 8:5, "Those who live according to the sinful nature have their minds set on what that *nature* desires; but those who live in accordance with the Spirit have their minds set on what the *Spirit* desires." So God designed us a certain way; we messed up the recipe through sin, and now we have to deny our desire for a perfect world and look to the Lord for any fulfillment that is available here on earth. Fortunately, He offers us all that we need to have an abundant life.

Illness makes us susceptible to such a wide range of emotions, especially when we encounter people who don't understand our illness(es). But Jesus says, "The water I give [you] will become in [you] a spring of water welling up to eternal life" (John 4:14). When those we love the most turn away during the darkest part of our life, we begin to well up with bitterness, confusion, and even envy. As we give into these emotions, we dilute Jesus' perpetual spring with our sewer water, and we well up with a host of destructive emotions that can turn us into "stinky" people.

We need to get a grasp on these emotions. "Hope deferred makes the heart sick" (Proverbs 13:12) — literally. Science has proven that a lack of hope can stall a recovery period from acute illness or surgery.

After more than a decade of living with a chronic illness, I know my limitations, but I've also learned to accept the limitations of others. One of the most freeing lessons I have grasped is to accept what people can offer without conditions or expectations.

This book isn't about the many people who just don't "get it" and how to change them. You and I both know that it's impossible for our loved ones to step inside our skin and feel the debilitating pain and tornado of emotions. There are some excellent books on how to reach out to those who have a chronic illness.[i] This book's purpose is to examine our own desires and then transform them so we can move forward in our spiritual growth instead of withering under the burden of unmet expectations.

That's what I believe God would want us to do — move forward. Nearly one in three people in the United States live with chronic conditions: asthma to scoliosis, diabetes to cancer. Some people will understand our predicament of living with daily pain more than others.

---

[i] *But You Look Good!* by Sherri Connell; *The Art of Helping* by Lauren Littauer Briggs; and *Helping Those Who Hurt: How to Be There for Your Friends in Need* by H. Norman Wright are excellent resources.

Regardless of how much or how little one understands, our next step is to learn how to progress from the whining and irritable, "How can I make people understand?" to being in total communion with the Lord. This isn't a feel-good book, but one that requires action, challenging you to look deeply at your own heart and its longings and then strive toward being the person that God wants you to be. Psalm 10:3-4 says, "[A wicked man] boasts of the cravings of his heart. . .in his pride the wicked does not seek [God]; in all his thoughts there is no room for God." We never want our cravings for validation to take the place of our cravings for the Lord.

While reading this book, certain people may come to mind and you'll think, *I wish he could read this. He really needs this!* But I challenge you to look at yourself with a new mirror, and see what changes God would like to cultivate in *you.* "Today, if you hear His voice, do not harden your hearts" (Psalm 95:8).

As Max Lucado says, "God loves you just the way you are, but he refuses to leave you that way."[3] Are you ready for a journey through the emotions of "but they just don't get it"? In Deuteronomy 1:6 God tells Moses, "You have stayed long enough at this mountain. Break camp and advance. . . ." Well, ready or not, we're advancing! We're going to move on down this mountain and jump the hurdles of our chronic illness journey that are misaligning us with who God calls us to be. He wants us off our rock of self-pity and self-absorption immediately. No hiking boots required.

Chapter 1

REJOICING IN GOD
What's rejoicing doing in this book?

"Rejoice in the Lord always. I will say it again: Rejoice!"

Rejoice. Not exactly how you expected this book to begin, is it? Take a deep breath with me. In. . .out. . . Now, say it out loud: "Rejoice. Oh, Lord, teach me how to rejoice." It's tempting to scan through the Scriptures directly to the part where God promises to save us from our plight; but there is a reason that thousands of passages begin with instruction or examples of rejoicing, praising, and worshipping our Lord: The closer we feel to God, the less significant the problems in our life seem.

Paul, the apostle who wrote these words, felt so convicted about the choice to rejoice that he emphasized, "I will say it again: Rejoice!" Surely, he anticipated that we would not give it the gravity it deserved, and he wished to stress its value. *Webster's Dictionary* defines rejoice: "To feel joy; to experience gladness in a high degree; to have pleasurable satisfaction; to be delighted."[1] However, the rejoicing that Paul is speaking of is not about simple gladness and delight, but a bewildering joy that a believer can experience despite the most adversarial circumstances—the kind that Paul writes about in Romans 5: "We rejoice in the hope of the glory of God. Not only so, but we also rejoice in our sufferings."

What? Rejoice in our sufferings? This is supposed to be a book about how I need people to understand what I am going through and how to make them be more sensitive.

19

I know. . .stick with me. Despite what seems logical, most suffering does have its upside. Even Helen Keller has admitted, "I have often thought it would be a blessing if each human being were stricken blind and deaf for a few days during his early adult life. Darkness would make him more appreciative of sight; silence would teach him the joys of sound."

How do we make the choice to rejoice? Bumper stickers encourage us to "Let Go and Let God." It sounds so simple. *To truly find the peace that we are seeking, however, we must be willing to let go of our human desire of wanting to make everyone understand.* And being able to surrender this over to the Lord requires some worshipping of who He is!

Carole Mayhall writes in *Words That Hurt, Words That Heal,*

> "More and more I am persuaded that what pleases the heart of God most are the choices we make that no one sees but God—those everyday moments when God is the only audience; when we offer to Him the sacrifice of praise; when the sweet aroma of our thanksgiving reaches Him. . . . When all joy is breaking loose in our life, we praise God with our heart, our mind, and our soul, but it doesn't take all the strength to do it. At that time, it's easy. But when our emotions are all negative, when circumstances make us want to scream—*then* praising God takes all our strength. And often our heart doesn't follow until later. . . . I think His 'Well done, thou good and faithful servant' will be spoken—or not spoken—when He recalls all the hidden moments of my life: the times I was tempted to grumble and complain; when I wanted to say, 'Hey, that's not fair! You didn't work that out the way I wanted You to.' The moments I said, 'I will praise You, Father. I don't understand, but I will thank You. I love You.'"[2]

Suffering Produces a Testimony

As we yield the wish to have everyone understand, through the act of surrendering to God's will, our intimacy with God immediately begins to escalate. The result is that the undesirable opinions and advice people offer carry less emotional impact, and we begin to discover opportunities within the conflicts.

By "letting go and letting God," we are essentially passing His test, which provides us with a testimony to share. When was the last time you cried out to the Lord when things were wonderful? We feel closer to God in the valleys than on the vacations. God's presence is closer when we're crying than when we're cruising. We must endure the test to have the testimony. If we are to share about the love, comfort, forgiveness, and peace of Christ, we must have experienced it; be confident in sharing your testimony! Rejoice with enthusiasm, because every time you share your testimony, Satan is defeated.

I believe that one of the reasons that I am sensitive to the verbal intrusions of people on the topic of my illness is because my illness is such a significant and crucial part of my testimony. When I share my struggles with daily pain, I also share the underlying strength that God provides to me. When I talk about my

"Most of the verses written about praise in God's Word were voiced by people faced with crushing heartaches, injustice, treachery, slander, and scores of other difficult situations."
—*Joni Eareckson Tada*

ministry, Rest Ministries, I am trying to explain the power and peace of God within the most undesirable circumstances. So, when people offer opinions on how I could get well and change my ministry to a "healing ministry," it *feels* like they are telling me that my testimony isn't powerful enough yet! It *feels* like they are saying God isn't "big enough" in my testimony, because I am not healed. Remember this: You are always an expert on your testimony. Although people may try to argue about it, your testimony is a gift from God and it cannot be disputed.

Learning to live with this thorn of chronic illness is not about you; or even your friends and loved ones learning how to relate to you. Your illness is about an opportunity God has provided for growth as He refines you in His image. Romans 8:18 says, "I consider that our present sufferings are not worth comparing with the glory that will be revealed in us." God has great plans for us! If we were to count the thoughts He has about us, it says in Psalm 139, they would outnumber the grains of sand. I gaze at my fourteen-month-old son sitting in his sandbox as he watches the sand sift through his fingers. He contentedly can do this for thirty minutes. Each handful is a new discovery. Imagine for a minute the number of God's thoughts, many of them *just* about you.

It should be noted that in Romans 8:18 it says that the glory in us will be *revealed*, not created. The you that God created, the you that He knew before you were formed in your mother's womb, will not be inherently changed by the refinement process, but God's glory will be revealed through you.[i] Right now, despite how you may feel, you have God's glory in you!

---

[i] Some of us may easily accept this refinement process and say, "Bring it on!" but for others this may sound overwhelming. If you struggle with depression, I advise you to seek help from a Christian counselor and perhaps even a medical physician.

An Odd Place for a Blessing

"A 'friend' recently asked me to help her with a wedding anniversary party at our church," shares Kelly. "I've had fourteen years of chronic monthly migraines and undiagnosed daily headaches. I told her that I wasn't sure if I could do it, but I would check my schedule and call her back. Her response was, 'Oh, are you going to have a headache that day?'"

Ugh! That comment was like a punch in the gut, but a blessing? Yes! Jesus assures us, just as He assured His disciples two thousand years ago, "*Blessed are you* when people insult you, persecute you and falsely say all kinds

> "*You intended to harm me, but God intended it for good to accomplish what is now being done, the saving of many lives.*"
> —*Genesis 50:20*

of evil against you because of Me. *Rejoice* and be glad, because great is your reward in heaven" (Matthew 5:11–12). Did you hear that? "When people insult you. . . *Rejoice!*" The next time someone says, "You must have sin in your life or God wouldn't allow this," take a deep breath and say to yourself, *I've just been blessed!* And here is a bonus: When we have an intimate relationship with Christ, we are more likely to recognize blessings. First Corinthians 2:14 says when the Spirit of the Lord is not within us, we won't be able to find the hidden blessings, ". . .[the blessings] are foolishness to [us], and [we] cannot understand them, because they are spiritually discerned." Are you in an intimate relationship with Jesus Christ? If so, you are likely less affected by people's comments.

Jesus says, "The insults of those who insult you have fallen on Me" (Romans 15:3). So you're covered, you're blessed, and you're safe. "In [His] dwelling [God] keep[s] [you] safe from accusing tongues" (Psalm 31:20). When we are abiding in the Lord, we are insulated from the emotional impact of negative comments. God knows how hard it is to bite your bottom lip and fight back tears. He knows you instinctively want to slap someone and that you're praying for strength to keep your arm by your side. "A fool shows his annoyance at once, but a prudent man overlooks an insult" (Proverbs 12:16). Rather than showing annoyance, recognize the blessing. It's much easier to overlook the insult when you know you are receiving a blessing. So. . . rejoice!

Isaiah 40:27–29 assures us that we have plenty of reasons to rejoice! "Why do you say, O Jacob, and complain, O Israel, 'My way is hidden from the Lord; my cause is disregarded by my God'? Do you not know? Have you not heard? The Lord is the everlasting God, the Creator of the ends of the earth. He will not grow tired or weary, and His understanding no one can fathom. He gives strength to the weary and increases the power of the weak." Regardless of how disregarded your life may seem by God, He is alive and well in your life. He is the everlasting Lord who never grows tired or weak. How wonderful to know that when we're exhausted, we can rely on His strength. Rejoice!

Review
- When we rejoice even when we don't feel like it, we're blessed.
- Suffering produces a testimony, and no one can disagree with your testimony.
- Blessings come in odd places, but if we are close to God we'll be able to discover them.

Reflection
- Have I lost the spirit of rejoicing in my daily life? What are some factors that have contributed to this?

- What are some practical things that I can do to rejoice in God?
- How have I noticed that my perspective on my problems changes when I really surrender them over to God?

Scripture
- "Wisdom brightens a man's face and changes its hard appearance" (Ecclesiastes 8:1).
- "May the God of hope fill you with all joy and peace as you trust in Him, so that you may overflow with hope by the power of the Holy Spirit" (Romans 15:13).
- "But let all who take refuge in You be glad; let them ever sing for joy. Spread Your protection over them, that those who love Your name may rejoice in You" (Psalm 5:11).
- "My soul will boast in the Lord; let the afflicted hear and rejoice" (Psalm 34:2).

Action
Surround yourself with thoughts that will help you rejoice in God. Read the Psalms, play worship music, pray the Scriptures, start a "Rejoicing Journal." As Renee Bondi mentioned in an issue of *HopeKeepers Magazine*, think about such things: "Whatever is true, whatever is noble, whatever is right, whatever is pure, whatever is lovely, whatever is admirable—if anything is excellent or praiseworthy" (Philippians 4:8). Make lists! You'll begin to feel better.

Prayer
O, Lord, teach me how to rejoice and praise Your name, even when my earthly instinct is not to do so. You are worthy to be praised. My problems become so insignificant when my focus is on You and Your glory. I

want to be able to see the hidden blessings You provide within the earthly discomforts. I want to pass Your tests so that I have a testimony to share. Lord, help my problems seem minor compared to Your love, and grant me strength and perseverance to rejoice at all times. In Jesus' holy name, amen.

Chapter 2

BEING GENTLE
But I am the one who had my feelings hurt!

"Let your gentleness be evident to all."

> "I have degenerative disc disease and had to have two fusions in my neck from the front. My best friend and her husband took my husband and me out to eat three months after my cervical disc surgery. I was very self-conscious of my huge scar on my throat and of the twenty-five pounds I had gained. At dinner, they asked me to come and sing with their church choir, but I said that since the surgery my vocal cords did not work right and I could not sing. The man looked at my face and then took a lingering look at my stomach and said, 'Well, it's probably because you have no support. It couldn't be the surgery.' I could have died!" —Nancy

Emotional wounds can hurt much deeper than physical ones. I believe that is why God tells us "apply your *heart* to instruction" (Proverbs 23:12). We would instinctively have our minds carry out God's commands and "instructions," but God knows it is more of a heart matter. One of the first steps to carrying out God's commands with our hearts is to learn gentleness and how to let it be evident to everyone. But this isn't easy. When our hearts are broken, the words we speak can become bitter. Matthew 12:34b says, "For out of the overflow of the heart the mouth speaks." It's important to take care of our hearts for the benefit of both ourselves and those around us. Our outward side can only fake it for so long before what's inside us seeps out.

"Look to my right and see; no one is concerned for me," says David in Psalm 142:4. "I have no refuge; no one cares for my life." We've all felt like David at one time—as if those we love are caught up in their own lives and that no one cares about the challenge it is just for us to survive each day of pain. The world has turned away from us. It's hard to treat everyone with gentleness when those we thought were concerned for us have offered empty consolation or have disappeared altogether. We're left feeling abandoned because of our wounds (Psalm 38:11).

> *"Never let a problem to be solved become more important than a person to be loved."*
> —*Barbara Johnson*

Why We Hurt

The thorn of chronic illness casts out everything we once defined as normal. We feel lonely and confused, but perhaps most of all, misunderstood. We feel like shells of our former selves. We have the same dreams and goals, but we can hardly get out of bed. All the stubbornness and self-confidence we possess—that always worked for us in the past—isn't making the pain go away. Our faith needs reexamined within this new definition of our lives. And we can't help but feel the "if onlys." If only people could...

Taste a small moment in our lives. . .
  Feel our fear of the future. . .
    Know pain twenty-four hours a day. . .
      Realize how horrible the side effects of the medications are.
      Have doctors disbelieve them. . .

We want to believe that *then* our sense of validation would arrive. Then we could move on and begin to live with the illness—then we could obey God's command to be gentle.

We just need to know people see us as we really are, not as whom we used to be, and yet, exactly who we used to be.

What We Need Is So Confusing!

It's very confusing, even to ourselves, what we want and need. Unfortunately, regardless of how clearly we can clarify the understanding we crave, that understanding is simply not going to happen. No matter how many times we try to explain or how many books we get people to read, they will never really get it. "It does no good to remind ourselves that our family and friends mean well," writes Crabb. "Try as we may, we cannot rid ourselves of the desire to have what no one has been given. We are dependent by nature."[1]

People who do not have a chronic illness will never understand what it's like to have a chronic illness. And because God designed each of us uniquely His, with our own set of life experiences, even someone who lives with the same chronic illness will never understand what it's like to live *your* life with *your* illness.

We Can't Change Other People

One of the hardest lessons to learn this side of heaven is that we cannot change other people. You may say, *What? I thought that was the whole point of this book.* But notice the title is *Why Can't I Make People Understand?* We need to understand what we *do* and *do not* have control over. More importantly, what are our motives? What do we seek to gain by having someone understand?

Even a simple "How are you?" can set various emotions off on a tangent, ending in bitter frustration. In *The Chronic Illness Experience*, author Cheri Register explains, "The 'How are you?' greeting is especially troublesome for the chronically ill because it presumes the possibility of improvement. At worst, it sounds like a test of achievement: 'Haven't you managed to shake this thing yet?' At best, its frequent reiteration shows how difficult it is for people to understand chronicity, that this illness will never be over but is, in fact, a constant feature of your life."[2]

"Real contentment must come from within. You and I can not change or control the world around us, but we can change and control the world within us."
—*Warren W. Wiersbe*

In our minds, we legitimize that we are justified in asking healthy people who still have their "lives" to sacrifice a small moment to reach out to those of us who have lost so much. It makes enough sense that Rest Ministries has a brochure: *When a Friend Has a Chronic Illness: What to Say, How to Help.* Healthy people may want to know how to reach out to you, so we provide tools. . . but they may not. . . . And then where are you left?

> "A distant family member told me that her daughter had been diagnosed with the same condition that I have, fibromyalgia," says Lenore. "She said the chiropractor who diagnosed her told her to ignore it and suggested that I do the same. Didn't help!"

People say hurtful things: believers, nonbelievers, everyone; I know I've stuck my foot in my mouth a few times! It's easy to put ourselves on a pedestal and believe we just ooze compassion, but Galatians 6:3–5 warns us, "If anyone thinks he is something when he is nothing, he deceives himself. Each one should test his own actions. Then he can take pride in himself, without comparing himself to somebody else, for each one should carry his own load." No one is perfect—not even you or I!

Testing Our Actions

Ask yourself, "Is this really a valid situation to get upset over?" Since my son was a newborn screaming over a diaper change, I would calmly say, "This isn't worth getting upset over." I'm sure he wonders what *is* worth getting upset about, since in his lifetime that situation still hasn't existed. Second Timothy 2:23–24 says, "Don't have anything to do with foolish and stupid arguments, because you know they produce quarrels. And the Lord's servant must not quarrel; instead, he must be kind to everyone, able to teach, not resentful." Before getting into a frustrating conversation with someone over your latest medical treatment, stop and ask yourself, *Is this a foolish or stupid argument? What are the odds that she will see my side and change her opinion?* Even if your instinct is to say, *I don't want her to change her mind; I just want her to understand,* let it go because this is an impossible expectation! In all likelihood, she will walk away and forget the incident while your blood may boil over it for hours, if not days. Besides, how does one measure how much someone understands or the amount of effort that is being put forth?

Secondly, in testing our actions, we must admit that we are not any more deserving of encouragement than anyone else. ". . .[a feeling of] entitlement destroys safety [in our relationships], because no normal human can fulfill our demands!" says Dr. Henry Cloud and Dr. John Townsend in their book, *Safe People.* "It's impossible to love an entitled person, as some fault, empathic misstep, or insensitivity will send the entire relationship tumbling down. The entitled person must be listened to and understood perfectly at all times, or she feels injured and wounded. The end result is isolation."[3] Do your thoughts begin with *But I. . .?*

But I don't ever feel good. . . .
  But I am allergic to the medications. . . .
    But I can't afford the medications. . . .
      But I'm still working part-time. . . .
        But I can no longer work. . . .
          But I'm not married with a spouse's support. . . .
            But my spouse doesn't understand. . . .
              But I'm so young. . . .
                But I'm so old. . . .
                  But I have so many children to take care of. . . .
                    But I have to deal with infertility too. . . .
                      But I can never make plans. . . .
                        But my schedule is so busy. . . .

We can all legitimize an attitude of entitlement, but we must choose to not claim this outlook. Everyone suffers on this earth, and no one gets through life without a few scars. We cannot demand sensitivity. In fact, when people demand sensitivity from me, my impulse is to turn and run. Their demands prevent me from having a desire to help or understand, because now what we have is no longer a friendship, but an obligation.

As my grandmother always said, "You're no better than anyone else, but you're just as good as everyone else." Test your actions. Although you may feel like a situation is all about someone else's sinful nature, it is really about your spiritual growth and accountability with God. It has nothing to do with anyone else.

> *"Nothing paralyzes our lives like the attitude that things can never change. We need to remind ourselves that God can change things. . .outlook determines outcome. If we see only the problems, we will be defeated; but if we see the possibilities in the problems, we can have victory."*
> —*Warren W. Wiersbe*

How do we test our actions? Ask yourself, "Why is it so important to me that someone really understands?" I recently had someone tell me, "I'm not looking for your respect. I just want you to understand!" I explained that as much as I loved her and would do my best to understand her, she'd never have that feeling of, *Oh, now she gets it!* I gently said that regardless of how much effort I put into trying to understand, it would probably never seem like enough. The affirmation she is seeking is not something that she can get from another person, but only from the Lord. I know I will disappoint her as I will fall short by leaps and bounds. I tried to explain that I will never be able to meet her expectations, but that doesn't mean I don't care. I will just try my best to be sensitive.

What is it that you need from other people? Your illness legitimized? Admiration for your positive attitude? Concern about your medical condition? Sympathy and attention because you're ill? (It's okay to be honest with yourself; most of us enjoy attention.) Do you struggle with losing your identity, and you still want someone to remember all you could once do? In an interview for *HopeKeepers Magazine*, Dr. Carter shares, "When you're so sick, and all your abilities are taken away, it's nice to know someone still remembers what you could do and still values you."[4] Are you searching for this and coming up empty? We will never be fulfilled if we aren't right with God. Micah 6:14 says, "You will eat but not be satisfied; your stomach will still be empty. You will store up but save nothing, because what you save I will give to the sword."

The Temptation of a Negative Attitude

Too often, we go through our day expecting no one to understand anything about us.

> You awake, wishing you could be doing something more important than you are. *No one understands what it's like to lose my career!*

> You pull out your medications and become depressed at the quantity of them. Then you realize you have to pick up a prescription later. *Ugh! I'll have to drive in the rain, plus this rain will make me flare!*

> Your child bounces onto your lap and you scold her that she can't do that to you. A friend calls and you let the machine get it. *She just doesn't understand how tiring it is to talk.*

> The mail arrives; since you were on the church's prayer chain last week—you've received two get well cards. *Why do people even bother? I'll never get well! It's chronic!*

> You pick up your Bible, but you're distracted; you want to take notes, but your hand is too sore to hold the pen. *Why do I even try?*

All this and it's not even ten o'clock in the morning yet! Are you feeling as discouraged as I am just reading this? Have you lived parts of it? I have.

How many times in your day does Satan negatively manipulate your thoughts about other people and their actions? How many times do you feel that sense of "no one gets it"? Could this be affecting your quality of life more than you realize?

High Expectations Are Not a Minor Offense

At the beginning of this book, I mentioned that some action would be required by you, the reader. Here's a big revelation that may influence you to change an attitude: According to author Larry Crabb, expecting people to fill a spot in our hearts that only God can fill is *idolatry*! Satan desires to move us as far away as possible from seeking God; he wants us to strive to fulfill our needs through worldly materials and relationships. First Peter 5:8 warns us, "Be self-controlled and alert. Your enemy the devil prowls around like a roaring lion looking for someone to devour." Satan wants us to search for happiness in unsatisfying ways: professional success, financial stability, the promise of health, and perfect relationships. Satan yearns to split families up, create confusion, distrust, misunderstandings, and have us avoid healthy communication. He wants us to destroy one another with cruel words and thoughtless actions, and maintain the burning rationalization that we're right and they're wrong.

It's a normal human emotion to wish for respect, to know we're valued and significant to someone, and to know that we make a difference. However, it's usually people that we seek these affirmations from—not God. When people are not giving us desirable responses, we become angry, bitter, and resentful. People will never be able to fill a hole that God designed in us that only He can fill.

In the book *Words That Hurt, Words That Heal,* Mayhall shares her husband's thoughts:

> "God has really been directing my heart to Psalm 62:5. It talks about putting my expectations in God alone. He seems to be saying to me that I can't expect any person to solve this situation. God is going to do it, and I need to expect nothing, except from Him."[5]

Jesus Himself told us that our relationships would be filled with strife—especially with people we love the most. Luke 12:51-52 says, "Do you think I came to bring peace on earth? No, I tell you, but division. From now on there will be five in one family divided against each other, three against two and two against three." Jesus isn't saying He wants strife! But He acknowledges that believers and unbelievers will have strained relationships.

But I'm a believer, you say. *And so is some of my family, but they're treating me poorly. They never consider what I can and cannot do; they are always pressuring me to just get a job and get my mind off my illness and it will go away. What about that, huh?* I know it hurts, but believers and nonbelievers both sin. You will find Christians who respond in less than Christian ways. In fact, sometimes Christians are so afraid of saying or doing something wrong, they don't do anything at all, while nonbelieving friends may be hanging out with us, bringing dinner, and asking us what we need. "Who can say, 'I have kept my heart pure; I am clean and without sin?'" (Proverbs 20:9). We are all sinners (Romans 3:23). "If we claim to be without sin, we deceive ourselves and the truth is not in us" (1 John 1:8).

> *"What we do in the crisis always depends on whether we see the difficulties in the light of God, or God in the shadow of the difficulties."*
> —G. Campbell Morgan

Our responsibility is to do all that we can do in our own lives and acknowledge that only God can convict others of the areas that need change in their lives. Hebrews 12:14 says, "Make every effort to live in peace with all men and to be holy; without holiness no one will see the Lord." Bottom line, even if we are justified and feel like we're the ones being abused, we must act holy so that people can see God within us. No one ever said being a Christian was easy.

"My family members are the ones who doubt my illness the most, and this really hurts!" shares Alice. "They have known me for so long; and they know that I have never been one to lie or be a hypochondriac, but they still ask me why I can't go on vacations or walk or do all the things I used to do. I have told them repeatedly and have even given them articles about fibromyalgia, but I wonder if they even read them. This hurts the most coming from my family."

Alice's lament is felt by many. Even David wrote in the Psalms, "If an enemy were insulting me, I could endure it. . . . But it is you, a man like myself, my companion, my close friend" (Psalm 55:12a–13). If it's any consolation, know that you are not alone. This is one of the reasons it is important to fellowship with other Christians, especially those who live with chronic illness.

Let's summarize: (1) By expecting others to "get it," you are placing expectations on them that God did not design for them to be able to fulfill. So let go of the need for them to have a reasonable conversation about the reality of your life; hence, you are surrendering your needs for self-worth solely over to God. You have now let go of that form of idolatry and will be blessed. (2) Now, make every effort to live in peace with them. That doesn't mean you have to sit and take abuse from anyone! But don't fight, throw bitter remarks back, or lose your cool. Remember, Peter described the first step of thwarting Satan's plan is to be self-controlled (1 Peter 5:8). Just calmly take yourself out of the situation. Leave the room, change the subject. Say, "I know you're just asking out of concern, but my illness is a very personal topic I'd prefer not to discuss. I'll let you know if there is anything you can do, okay?" and gently smile. Sometimes this will go over well, sometimes not. But you don't owe anyone an explanation.[i] Just be polite.

Understanding Different Friendships

The only way we will ever feel complete fulfillment in life and defeat the desire to have everyone understand will not come by changing other people, but by changing ourselves. We can do this by drawing near to God and rejoicing in who He is. Then we begin to feel His grace and mercy, and we're given a longing to pass this grace on to the people around us. We can accept them for who they are.

You'll find that some friends will become warriors alongside you battling your illness, and others will remain sideline spectators. Register explains in *The Chronic Illness Experience*, "There is a great deal of difference between advice offered out of a kindly ignorance and advice offered by someone who has learned enough about your illness to be watchful [for treatment options] with you."[6]

> "I have a friend of many years," shares Deb. "She really likes to 'help' by providing many articles and snippets that she thinks are related to my illness issues, usually from the newspaper or popular magazines. She has difficulty accepting it when I tell her that her current 'information' is not relevant to my problem(s). But she often refuses to move forward in our conversation until she finishes reading the article(s) to me. Sometimes I feel like her pet project."

Deb's friend has found purpose in Deb's illness, and she probably won't change. Deb has three options: (1) Continue to allow her friend to share the information and then just move onto another topic; (2) Gently explain her

---

[i] If this sounds challenging, I recommend reading *Boundaries* by Drs. H. Cloud and J. Townsend.

feelings to her friend, or give her a booklet, such as *But You Look Good!* by Sherri Connell, knowing that it may or may not change things; or (3) End the friendship, recognizing that if we begin to end relationships with everyone who does not understand, we will soon have few friends left.

When someone approaches us with a cure, our first response should be like the biblical warrior Joshua, who asked, "Are you for [me] or for [my] enemies?" (Joshua 5:13). It's hard to perceive people's motives at times, but the amount of grace we offer them should not be any different whether they are "for us" (and genuinely care) or "against us" (and seeking self-glorification in being a part of our healing.)

We offer both kinds of friends grace, and yet that doesn't mean we must trust them equally with our hearts. If you have not already begun to filter the information about your illness to those you speak with, you naturally will begin to do so soon. But let's look at our hearts for a moment.

The apostle Paul wrote, "This body of ours had no rest, but we were harassed at every turn—conflicts on the outside, fears within" (2 Corinthians 7:5). Have you experienced "conflicts on the outside"? For example, skeptical looks as you park in a handicapped parking space? Stares as you rise from a wheelchair at an amusement park? Or the parishioners who tell you to "just pray harder"? But how many of us have admitted our deepest fears about relationships within? Are you expecting intimacy and understanding from the same friends you purposely keep an emotional distance from?

> *"We are always seeking the reason. We want to know why. But God does not reveal His plan—He reveals Himself."*
> —Bob Benson

"Most of us are terrified to be open with each other, not because we're afraid of hurting or discouraging people, but because we profoundly fear that others will retreat from us. We hate to admit that the people we depend on are simply too weak to stay deeply involved once they face all that we are. We don't want to accept the fact that, since the Fall, no human being has the capacity to love us perfectly."[7]

Too often we are given the proof of this.

"Yesterday I had to go to the store for three things, but I wasn't feeling great, so I used my disability placard to park in a handicapped spot. No sooner did I get out than an older lady (I'm thirty-four; she may have been in her fifties) came by me and said, 'Well! You certainly don't look handicapped' with a sneer and walked away. I didn't reply; I didn't know what to say. But it hurts! People have no idea how difficult it is sometimes to shop, especially with my kids. It takes so much energy from me!" —Anita

But when we fear all people will respond to us in hurtful ways, we miss out on the special fellowship God desires for us.

"I am very sensitive about anyone knowing I am constantly in pain," says Pat. "We moved, and my pain was exacerbated about the time I met a new friend; and I desperately needed someone to comfort me. So I finally told her about my pain, and of my hesitancy to tell her and my fears of her reply, since so many people just didn't understand. Her reply changed my attitude forever: 'Why would you rob me of the joy of praying for you?' For the rest of my life, this one simple but majestic statement will affect how I empathize and pray for others."

Authors Cloud and Townsend remind us, "Be aware that when you're hurting, a voice may tell you, 'Why bother others? They'll see how weak you are. Where's your faith?'

It may be an idea planted by the Tempter to keep you from safe people."[8]

No human being has the capacity to love us perfectly. Imagine a world where someone always said the right thing. Your spouse always reads your mind, people know how to say, "How are you?" and when to say it, and how to respond to your answer. Imagine being given the grace, love, and appreciation you need seconds before you even recognize your desire for such things. Sounds absurd, doesn't it?

Yet each day many of us go out and face the world with one of two unhealthy mind-sets: (1) We have a naive hope that everyone will give us the exact validation we need in regard to our illnesses; and when this doesn't happen we end up hurt and disappointed; or, (2) We expect that no one will understand our predicaments, so we have low expectations of human nature to prevent ourselves from being hurt. This leads to a defensive spirit and a hardened heart that withers without joy.

What's Your Message?

What message are you sending in your style of relating to someone? "People who can't reconcile either their own or anyone else's faults suffer tremendous isolation because they are unable to attach to real, whole people who are both good *and* bad. The ideals of what 'should' be get in the way."[9] We often get back whatever it is that we give. Proverbs 11:27 says, "He who seeks good finds goodwill, but evil comes to him who searches for it." Life is what you make it. And it's a daily challenge to stay positive, because there are many times someone threatens to challenge that in an instant.

"I pulled into a handicapped parking space at the library," shares Phyllis. "A policeman immediately called to me and asked if the handicapped placard belonged to me. Instead of responding, I opened my door and swung my legs out. Immediately he could see my knee brace. I said, 'Polio.' He said, 'Sorry, I couldn't tell.'"

If we expect people to disappoint us, they will. If we expect their pity, they will give it to us. If we are joyful, they will reflect that back to us. Not always. . .but often.

It takes effort to have a joyous spirit when living with pain. God brings joy into our lives, but we have to endure the storms to get the rainbows. (Yes, it sounds corny, but it is true.)

"I have a wonderful friend named Veronika who always helps me out, driving me to doctors' appointments and things," says Joann-Marie. "She recently 'thanked me' for being a blessing to her. She said she is now more thankful than ever for the wonderful health that she has been given, and is encouraged by my faith because of all of my challenges. She also thanked me for allowing her to be the Lord's servant by helping me. How wonderful to hear those words, after having had other people say hurtful things."

"The way to love someone is to lightly run your finger over that person's soul until you find a crack, and then gently pour your love into that crack."
—*Keith Miller*

Many chronically ill people don't find these kinds of friendships, and it becomes easier to stay in their negative comfort zone. They still expect joy to enter into their lives, despite the fact they are only spreading a defensive "don't mess with me" attitude; this way, they have a reason to feel justifiably angry when people fulfill their expectations by disappointing them. Ecclesiastes 7:21–22 warns, "Do not pay attention to every word people say, or you may hear your servant cursing you—for you know in your heart that many times you yourself have cursed others." Translation: If you're going to be nitpicky about everything you hear, you'll hear all kinds of things you don't want to hear. We're all guilty of saying things we shouldn't have! I recently read the following: "There is so much good in the worst of us, and so much bad in the best of us, that it hardly becomes any of us to talk about the rest of us" (Edward Wallis Hoch).

Being Gentle

Now that we've taken a closer look at why we feel the way we do, how should our response of *gentleness be evident to all?* Oscar Wilde once said, "Some cause happiness *wherever* they go; others *whenever* they go." Which kind of person are you?

We can only loosely suppose how one can emotionally support us according to one's experience and knowledge—then we must give grace! If one is unwilling to try, we *still* must give grace. We all need grace. When I worked in the retail clothing industry, I waited on a very bitter, older lady. From the dressing room she snapped, telling me what to bring her. Everything I did was wrong. I dripped with sugar, showing her I could take her attitude. Hours after she left, her adult daughter, who had accompanied her on her shopping spree, called me at the store. "I just wanted to thank you for your kindness to my mother today," she explained. "She was diagnosed with cancer this morning, and I wanted to take her shopping for some pretty things to wear before her treatments start." We can only truly give grace when it's not deserved. *If grace is earned, it's not grace.*

"Rather than anticipate [your friends'] reactions, which is tantamount to controlling them, you must trust your friends to decide for themselves how fully they want to be involved in your fate. If they want in, let them in. If they prefer to back off a bit, let them. Unless you are honest with them and allow them to respond honestly, there is still a lack of trust at the heart of the friendship."[10]

"While in a major fibromyalgia flare-up with extreme pain and low blood sugar, I called 'Jane,'" shares Joanne. "I was too weak to prepare something for myself to eat and knew I would soon be passing out; in my incoherent state I wasn't quite able to express the seriousness of my condition, but Jane let me know she was disappointed that I had to cancel plans we had made. I suggested she might drop by, as I was at home. She said she was 'too busy for the next two weeks.' I called another friend who sensed in my voice that I was in distress, told me to lay down, take deep breaths, and that she would be right over. She came, stabilized my blood sugar, and spent the whole afternoon with me, even bringing a complete sugar-free snacks survival kit. I am so thankful to the Lord for friends who are sensitive to the leading of the Lord and follow through. When I felt guilty for having had to cancel on Jane, my friend reminded me that I had to take care of myself and that Jane probably had things on her mind and couldn't deal with that situation at the time. What a blessing she was to me."

We may have many good reasons to feel hurt, but according to Sheila Cragg, author of *A Woman's Pilgrimage of Faith,* "We give people with whom we're angry power over us when our animosity toward them consumes our thoughts and emotions. Our wrath can be more harmful than the offense that provoked it."[11] Joanne's friend did her a great favor by reminding her not to take Jane's response personally.

When we feel others provoking our emotions, we must remember to look the other way and give them grace. "Whoever corrects a mocker invites insult; whoever rebukes a wicked man incurs abuse" (Proverbs 9:7). Pray for discernment in how to handle your emotions and actions. This is far from easy. I've experienced personal attacks that have left my mind replaying the incident and searching my heart for what could have caused it and how I could have handled it differently. Each time, when the taste of bitterness would begin to arrive and the anger build, I'd pray, "Lord, please take my anger. Take away my bitterness. Give me a forgiving heart. I don't want to be this kind of person." I literally would put away the dishes and pray, "Lord, please take away this anger," as I threw each spoon into the drawer. It takes time, but God does answer the prayer.

The Bible's Answer on How to Respond to Unfair Suffering

First Peter 3:8-15 is an excellent example of instruction on how to respond in gentleness when you feel one has wronged you. Read it carefully and think about how you could apply each Scripture to your own life. I have bulleted it for easier application for your life, but it's word for word from the *New International Version* (NIV).

- "Finally, all of you, live in harmony with one another; be sympathetic, love as brothers, be compassionate and humble.
- "Do not repay evil with evil or insult with insult, but with blessing, because to this you were called so that you may inherit a blessing.
- "For, 'Whoever would love life and see good days must keep his tongue from evil and his lips from deceitful speech.
- "'He must turn from evil and do good; he must seek peace and pursue it. For the eyes of the Lord are on the righteous and His ears are attentive to their prayer, but the face of the Lord is against those who do evil.'

- "Who is going to harm you if you are eager to do good? But even if you should suffer for what is right, you are blessed. 'Do not fear what they fear; do not be frightened.'
- "But in your hearts set apart Christ as Lord. Always be prepared to give an answer to everyone who asks you to give the reason for the hope that you have.
- *"But do this with gentleness and respect."*

What God desires of us is the willingness to let go of bitterness and change the dynamic of the relationship. When He told us to "turn the other cheek," He wasn't saying to be a doormat but rather to give the person mercy, and watch what happens. When someone treats you harshly, he expects a harsh response. Perhaps by offering grace and calm, assuring words, you'll give him the opportunity to change if he so desires. Granted, sometimes people just want to fight, and our gentle words make them even angrier; but refuse to get into an argument. Speak calmly and quietly, and let them do most of the talking. In the end, you will be able to know you acted lovingly, despite the mud being thrown your way. Do your best to let the person see Jesus in you.

"There may be no trumpet sound or loud applause when we make a right decision, just a calm sense of resolution and peace."
—*Gloria Gaither*

We must remember that "there is one God and one mediator between God and men, the man Christ Jesus, who gave Himself as a ransom for all men" (1 Timothy 2:5). Jesus is the only One who can care for our emotional needs. He is the only bridge between the craving we have for value in this life and the fulfillment of it. When we look to Him for completion, not only is our own heart at peace, but we also reflect God's love and gentleness to all.

Review
- We can't change other people, regardless of how worthy our intentions may be.
- We need to test our own actions.
- Although a negative attitude may be understandable, God considers it sinful.
- Friendships will vary in levels of intimacy, but fellowship is vital to become whom God designed us to be.
- We must provide our friends grace, and seek validation *solely* from God.

Reflection
- When my feelings are hurt, how do I respond? Do I lash out? Cry silently? Feel victimized? How can I learn to be more gentle in my responses to those who mean well but cause me to hurt?
- Do I feel entitled to certain things because of my illness? What are they? How can I get rid of this attitude and replace it with gratitude for what I *do* have?
- Where do I search for my validation? Am I expecting too much out of people, rather than searching for my worth in Christ?

Scripture
- "A man's wisdom gives him patience; it is to his glory to overlook an offense" (Proverbs 19:11).
- "But you, O Sovereign Lord, deal well with me for your name's sake; out of the goodness of Your love, deliver me. For I am poor and needy, and my heart is wounded within me" (Psalm 109:21–22).
- "But in your hearts set apart Christ as Lord. Always be prepared to give an answer to everyone who asks you

to give the reason for the hope that you have. But do this with gentleness and respect" (1 Peter 3:15).

- "A gentle answer turns away wrath, but a harsh word stirs up anger" (Proverbs 15:1).

Action

Get a piece of paper. Write out 1 Peter 3:8–15 on the left side, and on the right side put your action steps. How can you best do what God commands? Apply it to specific situations or feelings you've encountered.

Prayer

Lord, I want to live with a heart of gentleness, not a spirit of bitterness. I know people will disappoint me, but help me love them unconditionally. Guard my own lips from hurting others. Grant me wisdom and patience, so I can overlook an offense as You would. Lord, since I've had to deal with this illness, I know I sometimes feel entitled to certain things: responses from people, materialistic things, even gifts from You. Help me remember to be thankful for all You've given me and help me always acknowledge that "every good and perfect gift is from above" (James 1:17). Teach me to be an ambassador for You who represents Your love and forgiveness. In Jesus' precious and holy name, amen.

Chapter 3

ACKNOWLEDGING GOD'S PRESENCE
Where is God when it hurts?

"The Lord is near."

It's easy to feel lonely when living with the isolation and fears of a chronic illness. Everyone, even those without illness, have those times of deep loneliness. In the book *Just Enough Light for the Step I'm On,* author Stormie Omartian shares her walk with loneliness.

> "I remember one particular time of great need in my life when I felt deeply lonely. It was the kind of loneliness that is so severe it brings physical pain as well as emotional agony. . . . One night, however, I was so overwhelmed that I turned to God. I lifted my arms and cried, 'Lord, why must I always be lonely? What can I do to get rid of this pain? You have promised to supply all my needs, and I need You to take this loneliness away.' The moment I prayed, I felt the arms of God surround me in an unmistakable way. . . . I have never felt loneliness like that since. . . . I now see any sign of loneliness as a call from God beckoning me to spend time with Him. I know He is not *causing* my loneliness. Nor is He *ignoring* it. He *sees* it and wants to fill the empty places of my heart with His love."[1]

You are a child of God. This is such a simple statement but with significant meaning. "It is He who made us, and we are His; we are His people. . ." (Psalm 100:3). Regardless of the bad experiences we've had as children, or the unfairness in our lives as adults, God is and always will be

49

in control. Years ago in Sunday school, I was taught that when things seemed overwhelming, take a deep breath and say, "God. . .is on. . .the throne." In Exodus 6:6 God says, "I am the Lord. . .I will free you," but the people of Israel were too angry and discouraged to listen to God's promises and encouragement. Instead, they focused on their past and whined about being victims of Moses and Aaron's grand scheme (Exodus 5:21). By choosing to be victims of their past, they destroyed their future.

Refuse to Be a Victim

"There is always a lot to be thankful for if you take time to look for it. Right now, I'm sitting here thinking how nice it is that wrinkles don't hurt."
—*Barbara Johnson*

How are you living your life? As a child of God or as a victim of man? We can't have it both ways; we can live as ones who are forgiven and offer forgiveness to others. Or we can be ones who are always distraught that life is not fair. People with this attitude always have an excuse or complaint, never choosing to accept any responsibility for their circumstances or their attitude.

By choosing this victim mentality, we're taking the power that God has in our life and handing it over to the person who hurt our feelings. Even more importantly, we must realize that we are handing over control of our life to Satan. John 3:19 says, "This is the verdict: Light has come into the world, but men loved darkness instead of light because their deeds were evil." All of our motives are given to us by either light or darkness, God or Satan. When you look at your motives, where are they coming from?

When the Israelites cursed Moses and Aaron, they missed out on God's blessings within the refinement process. When we're victims, we perceive everything as if it's done *to* us. Many of us with chronic illness(es) have experienced these emotions: *They were so rude! They don't understand that I can't shop all day! They told me I looked good! They forgot I couldn't walk stairs!* If you're a victim, the majority of your conversations may include. . .

I had to. . . .

  I didn't have a choice. . . .

   He made me. . . .

    You're lucky because. . . .

     I couldn't. . . .

      It was out of my control. . . .

       There was nothing I could do. . . .

Robert Schuller says, "Never let a problem become an excuse."[2] It's true that the Israelites had experienced difficult lives, just as living with an illness is unbearable at times. As slaves the Israelites were ruled over harshly by Pharaoh, but they identified so comfortably with the victim role that they were too distracted to hope in God's promise to save them. It's easy to remember our lives before illness as perfect, just as the Israelites said, "We were better off in Egypt." Sadly, in the end, the Israelites continual complaints and rebellion led God to ban them from the land that He had promised! Don't lose out on God's promises in your life just to indulge the chance to vent a bit.

When we choose the victim role we are claiming that: (1) We have no responsibility; (2) God does not have any power in our lives; our lives are just always messed up by others who treat us cruelly or unfairly; or, (3) *God* has messed up! None of the outcomes for these attitudes is favorable. God sees through any of our ulterior motives for wanting to be a victim, such as getting more attention. "All a man's ways seem innocent to him, but motives are weighed by the Lord" (Proverbs 16:2).

Ask yourself, "*Am I now trying to win the approval of men, or of God? Or am I trying to please men? If I were still trying to please men, I would not be a servant of Christ*" (Galatians 1:10). *Is being a victim and not having to take any responsibility an easier way to live? How do I benefit when I make people take care of my needs or feel sympathy for me?* If that's you, your emotions are understandable, but you've now taken ownership of this attitude. It's time to ask for forgiveness of trying to serve ourselves instead of God. And then we can move on! Without seeking repentance for our human desires, we're unable to live in communion with the Lord. We cannot serve God when we have a spirit of self-pity and self-indulgence. We cannot serve both God and ourselves, which is what we are doing when we are victims.

As Christ's ambassadors, we are to rejoice! But we're not called to rejoice because everyone thinks highly of us, or even because people see us as we really are. Our joy is to come from knowing God.

What Does Knowing God Really Mean?

God is always near you. Ray Bentley, pastor at Maranatha Chapel in San Diego, California, and author of *God's Pursuing Love,* says, "No matter how far you've run away from the Lord, He has always followed you. Just turn around." God loves us and knows we can have our thirst quenched by Him alone. Acknowledge that God is allowing this circumstance, and pray that He will reveal His purpose through the situation. Not necessarily reveal the purpose *of* the situation but *through* the situation. Why? The hurtful situation may feel very personal, but it's not about you. Romans 8:6 says, "Obsession with self in these matters is a dead end; attention to God leads us out into the open, into a spacious, free life" (*The Message*). Read God's Word, pray for discernment and wisdom in interpreting what you read, and ask God to be your strength. He is enough.

When you're close to the Lord, you don't need the other person to apologize in order to find peace, nor do you have to "get even" in order to have resolution. This is between the Lord and you. In *My Utmost for His Highest,* it says, "The knowledge that God has loved me beyond all limits will compel me to go into the world and to love others in the same way. I may get irritated because I have to live with an unusually difficult person. But just think how disagreeable I've been with God."[3]

God Is Faithful

Larry Crabb says, "Comforting thoughts about God's faithfulness can keep us living on the surface of life, safely removed from a level of pain and confusion that seems overwhelming. But God is most fully known in the midst of confusing reality. To avoid asking the tough questions and facing the hard issues is to miss a transforming encounter with God."[4] By claiming the victim role, rather than the child-of-God role, we're missing out on this transforming encounter with our Creator!

> *"God raises the level of the impossible."*
> —Corrie Ten Boom

My son is in the beginning stages of wanting to let go of the coffee table and take off walking. He knows I'm nearby and that he's loved and protected. The other day I sat and watched my son play. Suddenly he lost his balance and fell backward, bumping his head on a nearby toy. *Bonk!* He had that startled look and then silence as his little face scrunched up and began to get red. Then came the scream. I was already across the room, picking him up before any sound escaped. I held him, bounced him, sympathized with him, kissed his little head, smiled at him, and tried to distract him from the pain. In a moment it worked and the tears stopped.

So it is with God and us, His children. He's always there loving us, but until our lives go *bonk* we don't feel the intense outpouring of love that He longs to give to us. Like my son, we always want to get down from His lap and go "play." But when we hurt, He gets to lavish attention, love, and comfort on us. We are willing to cuddle up in God's lap while He dries our tears. If life didn't have the bumps and the bonks, we'd never get to be so lovingly comforted by our Lord.

Review
- By choosing to draw near to God, we're able to abandon the need to be victims who seek validation from other people.
- God sometimes "works undercover." He is always faithful and near, even when (or perhaps especially when!) we don't feel His presence.
- Without the bonks of life, we may never sit still long enough to really get to know God and receive His comfort.

Reflection
- In Deuteronomy 29, Moses reminds the Israelites that although they may have walked around the desert for years, God had been faithful in never letting their clothes or sandals wear out. How has God shown me His faithfulness in little ways, even during the difficult times?
- Have I ever felt rejected by God, as David expresses in Psalm 77? How did I (or can I) turn my attitude around like David did? What blessings do I hope to receive?
- In Judges 7, we find that when God has everything under control, even scary situations can become exciting. How have I experienced this sense of

exhilaration when circumstances should logically have led to fear?

Scripture

- "Praise be to the Lord, to God our Savior, who daily bears our burdens" (Psalm 68:19).
- The Lord upholds all those who fall and lifts up all who are bowed down" (Psalm 145:14). Read all of Psalm 145 to be encouraged.
- "What other nation is so great as to have their gods near them the way the Lord our God is near us whenever we pray to Him?" (Deuteronomy 4:7).
- "The Lord Himself goes before you and will be with you; He will never leave you nor forsake you. Do not be afraid; do not be discouraged" (Deuteronomy 31:8).

Action

How has God shown His faithfulness in your life? What is it that reminds you of God's presence? Increase this in your life, whether it's music, conversations with a friend, a new Bible study, prayer, or reading the Word. Do something specific that gives you an increased feeling of God's presence.

Prayer

Lord, it's so easy to get caught up in my life and the day-to-day challenges of illness. So many times I feel so alone, as though no one understands how hard it is to live with pain every day. I know You are always beside me, but sometimes I just don't feel Your presence. Lord, wrap Your arms around me so I can feel Your comfort. Provide me with faith in Your love so that during those times when I don't feel You, I still believe in Your presence. In Jesus' holy name, amen.

Chapter 4

LETTING GO OF ANXIETY
How do I really let it go?

"Do not be anxious about anything."

"An anxious heart weighs a man down, but a kind word cheers him up" (Proverbs 12:25). Most of us are familiar with Job, who had some understandably high anxiety. His heart was very heavy when he said to God, "You have closed their minds to understanding" (Job 17:4a). Have you ever felt that there was so little mercy on behalf of others that surely God must have closed off their minds to understanding?

You may even feel silly that you're making such a big deal out of longing to have people understand. After all, we don't understand a lot of our own friends' circumstances: the friend who just discovered her spouse was having an affair, the friend who just lost his job, (the one having daily treatments for cancer?), or the one who had a child diagnosed with autism. Do we understand his or her life? No. Yet we still feel that old adage, ("At least she's got her health!")Don't be tempted to put illness higher on the scale of suffering than others' suffering. I grew up hearing "everyone puts their pants on one leg at a time." In other words, we're all created equally by God, and we all matter to God equally. He knows that our unique personal hurts are huge—in our opinion—and He cares about each one of them. Whether it's an emotionally broken heart or actual heart disease, all of our pain matters to Him, and He longs to comfort us.

Character Building Is Never Easy

Henry Rollins once said, "Go without a coat when it's cold; find out what cold is. In times of hardship, you find out what you're made of and what you're capable of. If you're never tested, you'll never define your character." We know this to be true; the Bible says, "We also rejoice in our sufferings, because we know that suffering produces perseverance; perseverance, character; and character, hope" (Romans 5:3-4).

> *"Christ said we could move mountains if we had faith. But He didn't say we wouldn't need a shovel."*
> —*Joyce Vollmer Brown*

Perhaps you are trying to allow that character to build. Yet when someone says, "If you would just pray harder," your heart crumbles and character building is the last thing on your mind. Instead, you want to fight back! Someone once told me that when she parked in a disabled parking space, she got out and someone approached her and said, "You don't look handicapped to me!" Her reply was, "You don't look stupid to me." That may be just how her heart felt, but our hearts reflect our character (Proverbs 27:19). When our hearts are angered or frustrated, our characters are weakened. When we feel attacked, it's natural to defend ourselves but the Lord says, "Do not answer a fool according to his folly, or you will be like him yourself" (Proverbs 26:4). Learning to let go of anxiety and give it to the Lord is a step toward character. "The Lord will fight for you. . ." (Exodus 14:14). As much as you want to help the Lord, it's unnecessary.

Don't Worry about It!

> Susan, who lives with Tardive Dyskinisia says, "My illness
> affects my speech, facial muscles, and my cognitive abilities.
> I have had people say, 'Why don't you have more to drink,'
> 'She's really loaded,' and 'How many drugs have you
> taken?' Many assume I'm mentally ill or schizophrenic, and
> some are afraid of me."

When I read Susan's description, I couldn't help but think
of Hannah in the Bible, who confided to the Lord in her
heart with her lips moving but without voice, and the
priest said to her, "How long will you keep on getting
drunk? Get rid of your wine" (1 Samuel 1:14). But Hannah
quietly explained and didn't get angry. What self-control. I
don't know if I would have handled that as well.

The Lord tells us, "Do not be anxious about *anything*"
(Philippians 4:6). About anything! It doesn't say, "Do not
be anxious about the big crises, but the day-to-day ones are
okay; God's not as interested." It doesn't say, "Do not be
anxious about anything on the Sabbath." It says do not *ever*
be anxious.

Even God assures us that worry doesn't add a single
hour to our lives (Luke 12:25). He reveals this through the
words of Luke, who was a physician and likely witnessed
how stress affected one's life span, as we have scientifically
proven today. We're not to worry about what we eat,
drink, or wear. But more importantly, we're not supposed
to worry about how we will defend ourselves. In the
Gospel of Luke, Jesus explains how Christians will be
persecuted and how they should respond to their fears.
But let's look at the Scripture for a moment, and imagine
Him talking to you and me about our concerns regarding
defending our illness(es) to others.

"They will lay hands on you and persecute you. . . . This
will result in your being witnesses to them. But make up
your mind not to worry beforehand how you will defend

yourselves. For I will give you words and wisdom that none of your adversaries will be able to resist or contradict" (Luke 21:12a, 13–15).

Basically, Jesus is saying, "Don't sweat it! It's not worth the stress! Sure, it will happen. You'll feel harassed, but don't sit around and think about it and try to come up with clever little remarks that you can throw back at people. Instead, offer them grace, because you are a witness to them. And God will provide the words that He wants you to speak. If you allow yourself to let go of the need to speak your mind, and instead allow God to speak through your response, the Holy Spirit will use their ignorance or even rudeness to bring them closer to God Himself."

What good news!
- Although we may hear unkind remarks, this is to be expected. After all, we're all sinners and we've all said things we regret. Hope for the best in people, but don't be surprised when disconcerting situations arise.
- We can be confident that God has got it under control, and He trusts us to be witnesses on His behalf. When complete strangers approach you in the grocery store line and start asking personal questions about your cane (scooter, food selection, etc.), you have an awesome opportunity to share your faith. I think this is what is meant by Proverbs 14:10, "Each heart knows its own bitterness, and no one else can share its joy." We all have trials, but God makes something sweet out of the bitterness that no one else can fully comprehend.

How do we get to this place where we let the judgmental comments slide without experiencing roller-coaster emotions? What if we begin to share our testimony with someone in the grocery store line and she snaps back, "Well, I can see by your food choices you must not really care about getting well." (Yes, I've had that happen!) We must have a relationship with Christ that is so *intimate* that these remarks don't make us want to burn rubber out of the parking lot.

> "I was sitting in my car, in a handicapped parking spot, when a man knocked on my window and sharply reprimanded me for parking there. I pointed out the handicapped permit and he abruptly left. After a short cry and a talk with God, I forgave him and drove home." — Tricia

Without this deep personal relationship, you can know God, have a testimony, and still become enraged when someone begins to question your illness or faith. Confess your disappointments; then

"God will never reveal more truth about Himself until you have obeyed what you know already."
—Oswald Chambers

seek God's comfort. Crabb says, *"Until we acknowledge painful disappointment in our circumstances and relationships (particularly the latter), we will not pursue Christ with the passion of deep thirst. Or, to put it more simply, we rarely learn to meaningfully depend on God when our lives are comfortable"*[1] (italics in source). When we feel good, we have little motivation to search out God; when we feel badly, we whine to the Lord, *I don't want to read my Bible today. I'm too tired. I'm depressed. It's not making me feel any better anyway. You aren't answering my prayers!* But by complaining we're passing up an opportunity to cry out to God and allow Him to comfort us.

Sadly, Crabb says, "What we want simply is not there, but, as a fallen being, we naturally seek joy in every relationship except in our relationship with God. The result is inevitable frustration in our deepest parts."[2] *We naturally seek joy in every relationship except in our relationship with God.* And yet the only relationship that can provide the joy we seek is with the Lord. Ironic, isn't it?

Worry Leads to Destructiveness

Worrying *is* sin. "To spend an hour worrying on our knees is not prayer," says Oliver Barclay, author of *Whatever Happened to the Jesus Lane Lot?* How many times do we come to God in prayer with *just* worries? We forget to worship; we move right into the worries, and end with our want list. And then we quietly say, "In Jesus' name." This isn't really prayer! A Chinese proverb says, "The birds of worry fly above your head; this you cannot change. But that they build nests in your hair, this you can prevent." We'll always have a reasonable rationale to worry. But we must make a conscious choice to give the worries over to the Lord and not let their existence become a companion on our spiritual walk.

It's easy to become uptight over other people's opinions. Sometimes we don't even care if they agree with us; we just want them to take a mental moment to slip inside our skin and look at our lives from the inside out. We worry that people think we're lazy; we worry that they think we're crazy. We worry that they think we're being overdramatic, too withdrawn, underdressed, over-medicated, and even lacking in faith.

> "When I was unable to work due to as many as seventeen migraines a month and severe fibromyalgia, so many people from work told me they were able to work with headaches and fibromyalgia. It was upsetting to me to feel like maybe I was just weak and unable to deal with the pain that they seemed to hide with no problems." —Darlene

These feelings of anxiousness often lead into feeling anger. We're not getting something we need (affirmation); we're getting something that we didn't ask for (a strong opinion), and thirdly, the other person feels as if he or she holds the "truth scrolls." Many people in our lives believe that their emotions and their perspective on things *is* how things really are. God recognizes this attitude and says, "Woe to those who are wise in their own eyes and clever in their own sight" (Isaiah 5:21). We can easily get fed up!

God knows that we'll experience the human emotion of anger that He allowed us to have, but we're instructed to use it wisely. Ephesians 4:26 says, "In your anger do not sin." Remember, "Love is patient, love is kind. It does not envy, it does not boast, it is not proud. It is not rude, it is not self-seeking, it is not *easily angered*, it keeps no record of wrongs" (1 Corinthians 13:4-5). It doesn't say that love does not get angry, but that it's not *easily* angered. "Jesus demonstrated for us [in Matthew 21] what righteous anger looks like. It is controlled. It is focused. It is channeled into healing and helping, not destroying others. The purpose of righteous anger is to defend those who are defenseless. It is protective of others, not defensive of oneself or one's own ego."[3] Our goal is this: to love, to share Christ's salvation, and to honor Him with our actions and words.

It's a high standard to live up to, but God tells us, "If you do not do what is right, sin is crouching at your door; it desires to have you, but you must master it" (Genesis 4:7). Only with God's help can we master our natural sinful nature and show love. It's not easy, but "perseverance must finish its work so that you may be mature and complete, not lacking anything" (James 1:4). One of the first steps toward mastering sin is letting go of worry, anxiety, and our concern about what others think.

Overcoming Anxiety

We can overcome feelings of both anxiety and anger. How? Two ways: One, we have to ask God to test us! Psalm 139:23–24 says: "Search me, O God, and know my heart; test me and know my anxious thoughts. See if there is any offensive way in me, and lead me in the way everlasting." Secondly, God's Word instructs us: "Do not be anxious about anything, but in everything, by prayer and petition. . ." (Philippians 4:6). In other words, prayer is the answer to ridding ourselves of anxiety.

Worry is often considered to show the value of our love. "I love you enough to worry about you." Real love, however, trusts that God is always in control. Don't let anxiety weigh you down. God never designed us to bear our own burdens—but for us to surrender them over to Him to carry.

Review
- Building character is hard work and doesn't come without trials.
- Worrying about things won't change them, and it leads to destructiveness in our lives.
- God does not want us to worry. He has promised that He will take care of all of our needs (not our "wants" but our needs). We need to ask Him to provide a sense of peace in the chaos when it's tempting to worry.

Reflection
- How would those around me say I handle worry and anxiety? Does my worry prevent me from having a better quality of fellowship with the Lord?
- Do I worry about how my illness will or does affect my relationships? Do I worry about how I appear or am perceived? How can I surrender my worries over to God?

Scripture
- "An anxious heart wears a man down, but a kind word cheers him up" (Proverbs 12:25).
- "When anxiety was great within me, Your consolation brought joy to my soul" (Psalm 94:19).
- "So then, banish anxiety from your heart and cast off the troubles of your body" (Ecclesiastes 11:10).

- "Cast all your anxiety on Him because He cares for you" (1 Peter 5:7).
- "But make up your mind not to worry beforehand how you will defend yourselves" (Luke 21:14).

Action
Look up the following scriptural promises of the Lord and write them down on small cards. Place them around your home to remind you of God's faithfulness: *1 Peter 1:13; Psalm 31:24; John 14:27; John 14:1; Philippians 4:19; Psalm 4:8; Psalm 37:24; Nahum 1:7.*

Prayer
Oh, Lord, it's so hard not to worry. Even when I know in my heart that You have everything under control, my mind still wanders to the "what-ifs." Sometimes this illness seems to be more than I can bear. I worry about my family and how it's impacting their lives. I worry about my finances and how I will ever make it on my monthly income. I worry how much worse the pain will get and what I'll do if I can't get the medications that I need. Lord, I know You are faithful, but if You are really in control, why do I have so many burdens? Lord, take the concerns away and give me a lighter heart. Your Scriptures say, "Even the very hairs of your head are all numbered. So don't be afraid; you are worth more than many sparrows" (Matthew 10:30–31). Please help me see this promise in my life. Reassure me of Your love and faithfulness. I worry what will become of me, God. Help me trust in Your promise that I will have "hope and a future" (Jeremiah 29:11). In Jesus' precious name, amen.

Chapter 5

PRAYING AND PETITIONING
Finally I can make my requests known!

"But in everything, by prayer and petition. . ."

Okay, you say, I'm starting to understand how this works. I surrender it all over to God, He gives me blessings, opportunities, character, yada yada; but now is when I get to come to Him in prayer and petition. Thank goodness! I've been wondering when I would get to lay my needs out there!

Listen up, because you've got God's attention! First Peter 3:12 says "For the eyes of the Lord are on the righteous and His ears are attentive to their prayer." All you have to say is, *"Uh, God, are You there?"* and the Creator of the universe leans forward to the edge of His throne and looks to you with anticipation and joy about the conversation that you are to share. The Holiest of the Holies, the King of Kings, and the Lord of Lords is eager to hear from us! And we say, *This isn't the life I signed up for, Lord! I'm miserable. Nobody understands me! No one knows how much I hurt, and this life isn't fair. I'm just sick of it all! I want to be well. Now! Why, oh, why, are You doing this to me? What did I do to deserve this?*

Big oops!

There is a *big* difference between letting our hearts be known to God and wailing about our circumstances.

Hosea 7:13b–14 explains how God discerns between the two. "I long to redeem [you] but. . .[you] do not cry out to Me from [your] hearts but wail upon [your] beds."

When Petitions Turn to Demands

I've been in chronic illness ministry for nearly a decade, and during this time I've seen great confusion over the "prayer and petition" subject. Too often, our prayer time resembles a court case more than worship. First, we list our token thanks — we know we're supposed to start with worship, so we get that done. It kind of compares to getting a jury on our side right away. *Thank You, Lord, that I'm not worse off. Thank You, Lord, that I was able to awake today.* Okay, got that covered. Let's move on to the petition. We list what we need and then we make our demands. We plead our case to the Holiest of Holies as if we're attorneys convincing the judge and jury that our way is — beyond a reasonable doubt — justified and (mostly) truthful, so God should answer us in the way we've asked!

> *"If God, like a father, denies us what we want now, it is in order to give us some far better thing later on. The will of God, we can rest assured, is invariably a better thing."*
> —Elisabeth Elliot

Lord, I want to be healed! I deserve to live the life You intended, and I know that means You want me well!

And who of us has not at least once demanded, *Lord, give me patience and give it to me now!?* But Philippians 2:14 says, "Do everything without complaining or arguing. . . ." *Everything.* This includes praying!

It's too easy to demand things from God and call them prayer requests; excusing our attitude away by rationalizing, *"But He says to bring it all to Him! It's biblical!"* But we forget He is *Holy.* James MacDonald, author of

Lord, Change My Attitude (Before It's Too Late!), writes, "You are forfeiting the grace that could help you through the trial by complaining about it. All the grace and strength you need to experience joy and victory is available to you, but by choosing to complain, by clinging to the idol of a perfect life, you are flushing away the grace of God."[1] Wow! I know that's a compelling reason for me to watch my attitude.

Not only do we make demands, but we often do it in a spirit of anger. *I'm extremely mad about this illness and I'm not too pleased with God either. It's okay to get angry with God. God got angry with people! If God wants my intimacy, He needs to hear my complaints.* But it's not okay. It *is* sin, and we refuse to acknowledge it as such. Look at how God dealt with anger (Job), arrogance (Moses), pride (King Uzziah, who was given leprosy), and evasion (Jonah). A demanding spirit is not something God takes lightly.

Responsible Anger

I'm not saying that anger directed at God is not allowed and to be a real Christian you won't ever feel these emotions. But never forget your emotions are being hurled toward the King of Kings.

In *How to Be Like Jesus: Lessons on Following in His Steps*, it reminds us of what our Savoir endured; He could have easily chosen a different attitude. "Consider the human disappointment Jesus endured; rejected in His hometown, harassed and persecuted by the religious leaders of His nation, misunderstood by His own family, betrayed with a kiss, and abandoned by all His followers. Yet through it all Jesus never complained or rebelled against God; He trusted God even on the cross."[2]

Remember, God is Holy with a capital "H." First, God says, "In your anger do not sin" (Psalm 4:4). He even goes on to advise us how to deal with the anger: "When you are on your beds, search your hearts and be silent" (in comparison to wailing on our beds, Hosea 7:14). Go take a good flop on the bed, search your heart, gently tell God why you are hurting, and then be silent. Let it go! We must quit rationalizing why we deserve to lose our temper with the Lord.

> *"I will never forget the day I was saved. A man looked at me and said, 'Why don't you quit telling God what you want and tell Him that Jesus Christ is all you need.'"[3]*
> —Kay Arthur

I have often read in Christian books how we can "let loose" and get angry at God. The books say, "God can take it." Yes, God can take it; your bitterness will not destroy the Almighty. But the real question to ask yourself is can you take God's response to your wrath? Your attitude hurts Him deeply. His response to Job's waving fists was less than pleasant for Job. "The Lord spoke to Job out of the storm" — (imagine a thunderous voice) — "Brace yourself like a man; I will question you, and you shall answer Me" (Job 40:6-7). Are you prepared for God to respond to you after you've spoken to Him? Read Job 40 and 41 before outpouring your anger. God also says, "He who guards his lips guards his life, but he who speaks rashly will come to ruin" (Proverbs 13:3).

Secondly, it's nearly impossible to honor God while being angry with Him at the same time, and not honoring God and who He is *is* sin. Look at Moses, who slapped a rock with his staff to retrieve water—when God had instructed him to speak to the rock. He had a bit too much attitude. God's response: "Because you did not trust in Me enough to *honor Me as holy* in the sight of the Israelites, you will not bring this community into the land I give them" (Numbers 20:12). Instead of admitting his sin, Moses blames the Israelites for his exclusion from inheriting the Promised Land. Right before his death, God reminds him again, "This was between you and Me! There on the mountain that you have climbed you will die. . .because you broke faith with Me in the presence of the Israelites. . . because you did not uphold My holiness among the Israelites" (Deuteronomy 32: 50–52, summarized).

Moses' sin was a lack of respect for the holiness of the Lord and too much attitude—specifically, he did not honor God as holy; he had lost the fear of God that he had experienced earlier in his ministry, thus Moses also lost his respect of God. And consider this: According to Scripture, Moses wasn't an uppity kind of guy. "Now Moses was a very humble

> *"We can do nothing, we say sometimes, we can only pray. That, we feel, is a terribly precarious second-best. So long as we can fuss and work and rush about, so long as we can lend a hand, we have some hope; but if we have to fall back upon God—ah, then things must be critical indeed!"*
> —*A. J. Gossip*

man, more humble than any-one else on the face of the earth" (Numbers 12:3). Upholding God's holiness and being a trustworthy witness for the Lord in front of others is obviously important to God, and if the most humble man on earth had some trouble with it. . .well, let's just say I know to keep a short rein on any rebellious emotions I may have.

Examine how your attitudes can affect your prayer time. What does God see when He watches your actions and attitudes? First Chronicles 28:9 says that the Lord searches every heart and understands every motive behind the thoughts. Is your motive to honor the Lord or to relieve yourself from discomfort? I believe in his heart, Moses was in awe of God, the Lord Almighty, but he didn't depict this in his actions. He was also surrounded by people he was to witness to. This is important: God still held Moses accountable for his actions, despite the fact that they may not have represented Moses' true feelings, but just emotions let loose under stressful circumstances. Be mindful that if you decide to lose your temper, God will forgive you when you repent, but He may still hold you accountable, regardless of the circumstances that may have led up to the event.

The Confusion of Answered Demands

Occasionally, we demand things of God—and He gives them to us! How confusing! We're like a whiny child in the grocery store line that wants candy. I've seen an exhausted mom just give in because she is tired of hearing her child incessantly beg. "Fine, have the candy!" she says, and then later the child has a horrible stomachache. The Israelites whined that they wanted meat—to such an extent that the Bible tells us that every family stood outside the entrance to their tents and wailed! (Numbers 11:10). Imagine the sound of 2 million[i] people standing around wailing across the desert, howling, "We were better off as slaves. We want meat!" So. . .God sent them quail, even though He was "exceedingly angry" (Numbers 11:10). They whined and got their way, right? Oh, but be sure to read the rest of the story! "While the meat was still between their teeth and before it could be consumed, the anger of the Lord burned against the people, and He struck them with a severe plague" (Numbers 11:33). It appears that God said "Fine, you want meat! I'll give you meat!" *Zap!* But He was exhausted by their complaints and demands; He was discouraged and disappointed in their lack of trust for Him to provide what was necessary. So God answered their "prayers," but then He withdrew Himself.

Too often the story of the quail is told as an example of God's faithfulness: His people prayed for meat and God gave them meat, making sure His people were fed in the

---

[i] This number varies according to sources, from 600,000 to 2 million.

desert. This is incorrect. The manna was God's provision for their needs. But the people complained about the manna and demanded the quail. The quail are an example of the repercussions of making demands of God.

We could look at this and say, *But that was back then. God sent Jesus to die for us and He's not nearly that picky anymore. He wants my honesty, right? He doesn't want me to be fake, does He? I'm no Pollyanna. Illness is horrible! I'm just asking for what is mine!*

My response is this: First, "Jesus Christ is the same yesterday and today and forever" (Hebrews 13:8). So, although Jesus paid the price for our sins, losing our temper with the Almighty and not honoring Him *is* still sin. After the sacrifice Jesus made for us by dying on the cross, we should feel even *more* respectful of the Lord. God

> *"Adversity is always unexpected and unwelcomed. It is an intruder and a thief, and yet in the hands of God, adversity becomes the means through which His supernatural power is demonstrated."*
> —*Charles Stanley*

doesn't grade on a curve, averaging out human behavior from past centuries. The actions, thoughts, and motives of the Israelites that made Him "exceedingly angry" thousands of years ago still make Him burn with anger.

Secondly, I believe that God *does* want us to be honest. He says, "But in everything, by prayer and petition, with thanksgiving, present your requests to God" (Philippians 4:6). But notice the *"with thanksgiving"* part. We could change these words to "with an attitude of gratitude." Satan loves to see us raise our fists to the Lord. He thrives on watching us treat the Lord with a lack of reverence or holiness. And more than anything, he enjoys hearing us get mad at God and then excuse it away with, "But He wants me to be honest, right?"

Satan thrives on seeing us rationalize sin. John 10:10 says that Satan comes to "steal and kill and destroy." One of his great successes is to see us destroy our own faith by making exceptions to God's commands. Satan wants us to find understandable reasons why we can speak to God without any fear of the Lord. From the beginning of time, when Satan approached Eve, he has tried to convince human beings that we do not need to fear God. God doesn't want our excuses — or even perfection! He wants a humble spirit.

MacDonald says, "Problems may fuel a demanding spirit but never justify it. God is unalterably opposed to a demanding attitude on the part of His creatures no matter how severely they're suffering. His ears are open wide to hear cries of laments and pleas for help, but He will not come to a negotiating table to consider terms from angry people. God opposes the proud who demand, but gives grace to the humble who express their hurt."[4]

What Has Happened to Our Fear of God?

When we demand things of God we're telling Him, *"You've messed this up and now You need to fix it!"* Be forewarned, however; no one tells God what to do! Psalm 111:10 gently reminds us that "the fear of the Lord is the beginning of wisdom." What's happened to all of our fear? Remember how we just discussed swallowing our pride and saying, "Lord, change *me*"? Psalm 55:19b tells us that "men who never change their ways. . .have no fear of God."

There is a big difference between making prideful demands of God and humbly expressing your hurt. "You hear, O Lord, the desire of the afflicted; You encourage them, and You listen to their cry" (Psalm 10:17). It doesn't say God will listen to the *demands* of the afflicted, but the cries. If the difference is still confusing ask yourself, "Is this a prayer I can make on bended knees with my hands turned upward to God? Or is this a prayer where I instinctively stand and shake my clenched fists at the sky?" This is an easy way to gauge whether your attitude is filled with humble submission or angry demands.

God desires us to fear Him. People often wonder why He wants us to be intimidated by Him yet intimate with Him at the same time. I believe God wants us to fear Him by having a healthy respect for Him and by always being aware that He is God and that He is the final authority on whether we see tomorrow or not. God wants us to "[speak] the truth in love," — not only to others but to Him! Then "we will in all things grow up into Him who is the Head, that is, Christ" (Ephesians 4:15). If fearing the Lord is a difficult thing for you to understand, ask God for insight. Proverbs 2:3-5 says, "And if you call out for insight and cry aloud for understanding, and if you look for it as for silver and search for it as for hidden treasure, then you will understand the fear of the Lord."

At Risk of Making Demands

Many people with illnesses have taken a moment to reflect on the life of Job. Job is perhaps the man whom we feel we can best relate to; Satan attacked him, and he withstood the blows. As he lost his family, possessions, and wealth, still he praised God; and even when his health was taken, Job 2:10 tells us, "In all this, Job did not sin in what he said." Eventually, after being on the receiving end of what he felt were some judgmental comments from his friends, he began to lose his patience. Crabb confirms that when we are hit hard by a series of difficult events this is a normal response, but we must watch our response carefully. *"When things do not go well, especially for an extended period of time, when our heart is filled with more pain than joy, the temptation to let our desire for relief becomes a demand that is strongest*"[5] (italics in source).

Job went through a series of emotions following this attack. At first he said, "Though one wished to dispute with [God], he could not answer Him one time out of a thousand." (Job 9:3). Then he began to become depressed and decided to tell God how he felt, bitterness and all. He exclaims, "I loathe my very life; therefore I will give free rein to my complaint and speak out in the bitterness of my soul. I will say to God: Do not condemn me, but tell me what charges You have against me" (Job 10:1-2). Still later he becomes very bold, now believing that he has a case against the injustices: "I desire to speak to the Almighty and to argue my case with God" (Job 13:3).

Frustration, bitterness, a lack of the fear of the Lord — they are all a slippery slope, and when we tell God how we feel in a spirit of anger, we're setting ourselves up to grow into a demanding spirit. God deals with this justly, as He did with Job's accusing attitude and demands for healing: "Would you discredit My justice? Would you condemn Me to justify yourself?" (Job 40:8), or in *The Message* it says, "Do you presume to tell Me what I'm doing wrong? Are you calling Me a sinner so you can be a saint?" "[God] looks down on all that are haughty; He is king over all that are proud" (Job 41:34). In other words, God told Job, "Stand up and take it like a man! Who do you think you are?" (see Job 40). Job realized what he'd done and replies, "I am unworthy — how can I reply to You?" (Job 40:4). Henry Ward Beecher, a nineteenth-century preacher, once said, "Speak while you are angry and you'll make the best speech you'll ever regret."

Ask yourself, "[Is my] 'trust' in God rooted in unconditional confidence in His character and sovereign plan but rather in a hope that [He'll] relieve [my] suffering in the way [that I desire]?"[6]

But Life Is So Unfair!

One of the reasons that we can feel so justified in making demands is that we're just trying to level out the playing field of life. It seems so unfair. Our healthy friends surround us, driving their fancy cars and going off on their exotic vacations. Scripture speaks specifically of this: "For I envied the arrogant when I saw the prosperity of the wicked. They have no struggles; their bodies are healthy and strong. They are free from the burdens common to man; they are not plagued by human ills" (Psalm 73:3-5). But consider this: Perhaps they are making demands of God and maybe God is responding to their demands – but there is a price. In Psalm 105:40 King David speaks of God's great loyalty in providing quail for the Israelites, but there is no mention of the plague that God sent afterward. We must not be quick to believe that everything comes easily for those around us. Like David, we don't see the plague in their lives that follows.

How do we fight this natural response of wanting to throw our fists up toward the heavens and shake them? First, recognize that when you shout your angers to the Lord, the devil is rejoicing. Affliction is a spiritual battlefield. "Put on the full armor of God so that you can take your stand against the devil's schemes. For our struggle is not against flesh and blood, but against the rulers, against the authorities, against the powers of this dark world and against the spiritual forces of evil in the heavenly realms" (Ephesians 6:11-12).

Secondly, stay convicted of God's holiness. "Let us not become weary in doing good, for at the proper time we will reap a harvest if we do not give up. Therefore, as we have opportunity, let us do good to all people, especially to those who belong to the family of believers" (Galatians 6:9-10). Maintain a healthy fear of the Lord: "To fear the Lord is to hate evil" (Proverbs 8:13). When we fear God, we have discerning hearts to know what is pure and what is evil. The fear of God is a choice that we make and with it comes great rewards (see Proverbs 1:28-33).

How to Pray

So, how do I pray? I want to be honest with God, but I don't want to do anything wrong! First, don't stop talking to God. God says, "I wish you were either [hot] or [cold]" (Revelation 3:15). If, after understanding all that you've read, the only emotion you have to express is still anger, let it out, but be in control of it. Don't avoid God until you are feeling better, or you may never talk to God again. We can't heal our emotions — only God can. However, stay motivated to get past the anger as soon as possible. Too many people have a spirit of anger about their illness for decades. Don't get stuck there. You'll face a life of loneliness and be susceptible to the lessons God will teach you about surrender.

> *"There is no success without sacrifice. If you succeed without sacrifice, it is because someone has suffered before you. If you sacrifice without success, it is because someone will succeed after."*
> —Rick Joyner

There are many Scriptures in the Bible that can point you in the right direction for a quality prayer life, as well as some wonderful books on the subject. According to Webster's Dictionary, to petition means "to make a prayer or request to; to ask from; to solicit; to entreat; especially, to make a formal written supplication, or application to." Basically, we're supposed to explain to God what it is that we desire — but with an attitude of honor for what we believe God *wants* us to have — so we can be the people He

wants us to be. In *How Can I Pray When I'm Sick?* author
Douglas Connelly shares his thoughts:

> "Today when I visit someone who is sick or who is facing
> surgery or who has been diagnosed with an incurable disease,
> I ask God in prayer to heal that person. I don't demand
> healing; I ask for it. My prayer isn't an arrogant or showy
> command; it is the humble cry of a child of God. I also
> acknowledge when I pray that God is far greater and wiser
> than I am. I ask for his healing, but I also submit to his will.
> I've been challenged a few times about praying like that. One
> man told me that when I pray 'if it be your will,' I am
> demonstrating a lack of faith. He, of course, believed that it
> was *always* God's will to heal. As I looked at Scripture,
> however, I disagreed with his conclusion. Sometimes when
> God allowed faithful believers to become sick, it was clearly
> his will. When we ask God to do something 'if it is his will,'
> we are simply confessing that we don't know with certainty
> what his will is in this particular situation. . . . Prayer is not
> our manipulation of God. Prayer is a conforming of our will to
> his will. Sometimes when we ask God to heal 'if it is his will,'
> he will grant that request. . . . Sometimes God will begin to
> change our hearts so that we ask for something else—our
> request is conformed to his will. Sometimes God will not grant
> our request but leads us instead to rest in his wisdom and
> care."[7]

Let's look at a few major attitudes our prayers should
include:

Pray for contentment
Pray for contentment in Jesus Christ rather than for others
to change to accommodate your needs better, because "a
heart at peace gives life to the body, but envy rots the
bones" (Proverbs 14:30). Crabb says, "We tend to measure
someone's love by their degree of cooperation with our
plans."[8] But perhaps, more than with people, we do this
with God. *If He isn't answering my prayers, He must not really*

love me! But be careful. This is a serious test of the Lord God, and He doesn't put up with our tests (Luke 4:12). If you're still tempted, just read about the forty years the Israelites spent in the desert. Over and over they tested God, and over and over they lost their very lives. Contentment gives one so much freedom to live. Ask God for a contented heart in any circumstance. Contentment can be learned, according to the apostle Paul (Philippians 4:11).

Pray "Thy will be done. . . ."

Jesus Himself prayed these very words on the Mount of Olives right before His death, "Father, if You are willing, take this cup from Me; yet not My will, but Yours be done" (Luke 22:42). In the Gospel of Luke, in the very next verse, it says, "An angel from heaven appeared to Him and strengthened Him" (v. 43). Surrendering to "Thy will be done" is always difficult; yet when we get those words out, God always provides strength for us to handle whatever He sends our way.

Pray for your needs

In Matthew 6:9-13 God gives us an outline for how to pray: "Give us today our daily bread" (v. 11). Notice that Jesus specified bread, which is a part of our essential diet, reminding us to pray for that which we need, not that which we crave or desire. It doesn't say, "Give us this day our daily nachos and milkshakes." This could be seen as covetousness. What do we really need from the Lord? Our prayer should be to ask God to work in our lives to refine us to be more like Him.

Pray for those you love

We are certainly called to pray for those we love and that God strengthens and empowers them; but are we praying this for their benefit or our benefit? To keep focused on praying for others' needs, it can be helpful to pray a particular Scripture, inserting his or her name into it to make it personal.

Pray to be changed

Avoid the temptation to pray, "Change Aunt Mary and change my brother—he really annoys me too, God. Can You believe he had the nerve to say that to *me*?" Let go of expectations. Mark Cosgrove, author of *Counseling for Anger* says, "Irrational expectations or beliefs. . .are often a refusal to accept reality because we want things to be different for our own convenience or purposes."[9] We must take a deep breath and say, "Lord, change *me*. Help me to be less sensitive. Guard my heart from the pain of hurtful comments. Let me reflect Your love to people around me so they can see You better."

Pray for forgiveness

We all fall short of perfection and to keep our relationship intimate with God, prayer must include repentance. Most of us have demanded things from the Lord, but He has a forgiving heart if we come to Him as the psalmist did: "When my heart was grieved and my spirit embittered, I was senseless and ignorant; I was a brute beast before You. Yet I am always with You; You hold me by my right hand. You guide me with Your counsel, and afterward You will take me into glory" (Psalm 73:21–24).

> *"Things will never be the same— they could actually turn out better."* —
> *Jan Johnson*

Pray for God to test your heart

It's not about how the world treats us; it's about how we respond to the world and how we relate to our God. We may suffer from people's insensitivity, ignorance, unkindness, and prejudice. In comparison with the sins of those around us, our sin of asking for understanding seems so trivial! But it's our responsibility to take our hearts to God and lay them out there and ask Him to search them and reveal His findings.

Who wants to do that? It's rarely done by most Christians. When life is going smoothly why stir things up? Why ask God to search our hearts and then have to deal with His findings? After all, when someone hurts our feelings, and we're in tears and have done all we know how to do — and they *still* see the worst in us — it doesn't seem like a fair time for God to start digging around in our hearts, does it? We've been wronged! We're hurting! We've just been provided a list of character traits we need to work on by someone who supposedly loves us, and the last thing we need is a list of poor character traits from God. So the outcome is that we don't ever take the time to ask God to search our hearts. We never create that intimacy with the Lord.

It's a scary thought to say, "Test my actions, Lord," because the likelihood that God will say, "All clear! Couldn't find a thing to work on," is pretty slim. But guess what? Whether we ask Him or not, He still searches our hearts: "I the Lord search the heart and examine the mind" (Jeremiah 17:10). It's like a credit report. Even when you know you may find some negative marks, it's still better to know what those in charge of giving you credit know. We're also called to personally search our own hearts: "In your anger do not sin; when you are on your beds, search your hearts and be silent" says Psalm 4:4. We're usually angry because we feel wronged, and yet the first thing we're told to do is *not* to approach the person or talk about it with someone else. We're to go to our private place where we can think and pray and search our own hearts. Why be silent? Because only then will we be able to hear God's voice.

Trusting God to Answer

Oliver Barclay says, "Indeed, there are times when it is our duty, having committed a problem to God in prayer, to stop praying and to trust and to do the necessary work to arrive at a solution." I believe what he means is that at some point we have to get up from our knees and leave the house. God doesn't need our help; we must move forward and trust that God will lead us to where He wants us to be.

Actually, did you know that the Bible specifically says what God wants from us? It's captured in one simple verse that is easy to memorize and cling to during confusing times. Micah 6:8 says: "And what does the Lord require of you? To act justly and to love mercy and to walk humbly with your God." Because of God's great love for us, we have nothing to fear. "Do not fear what they fear, and do not dread it. The Lord Almighty is the one you are to regard as holy, He is the one you are to fear, He is the one you are to dread, and He will be a sanctuary. . ." (Isaiah 8:12b–14a).

Review
- We must understand the difference between petitioning God and demanding things of God.
- Demands made of God may be answered but with disadvantageous results.
- The fear of God is an essential part of worshipping who He is.
- Comprehending how to pray will draw us closer to God.

Reflection
- Is my motivation to honor the Lord and His will for my life or to ease my discomfort?

- Am I at risk of not honoring God as holy like Moses did? Do I complain or petition God? How do I feel after being angry at God? How do I feel after petitioning Him for His will?
- How can I adjust my prayer life to reflect a reverence for God?

Scripture

- "We all stumble in many ways" (James 3:2a).
- "What causes fights and quarrels among you? Don't they come from your desires that battle within you? You want something but don't get it. You kill and covet, but you cannot have what you want. You quarrel and fight. You do not have, because you do not ask God. When you ask, you do not receive, because you ask with wrong motives, that you may spend what you get on your pleasures. . . . Submit yourselves, then, to God. Resist the devil, and he will flee from you. Come near to God and He will come near to you. Wash your hands, you sinners, and purify your hearts, you double-minded" (James 4:3, 7–8).

Action

When was the last time you spoke to God from your knees? Sometimes our illness prevents us from physically getting down on our knees, and in turn it can impact our prayer life. If you're able to get down on your knees, do so; if not, that's okay too. But have a conversation with God as you would a good friend, keeping your hands turned upward while speaking to Him. Feel the difference in your prayer time.

Prayer

Lord, it seems that since I've become ill praying has become so complicated. Do I pray for healing? Less pain? Wisdom? Am I being punished or disciplined through my illness like people suggest? Or is it just the result of living in a fallen world? I get so many conflicting messages. Lord, I trust that You know I want to be well; but You also know that more than that, I desire Your will for my life. I pray for this thorn to be removed from my life, but also give me the grace to endure it for however long You let it stay. Test my heart and reveal to me Your findings. Help me grow more like You, Lord, even if it means sharing in Your sufferings. Give me the strength to endure it and use it for Your glory. In Jesus' name, amen.

Chapter 6

GIVING THANKS
But I have an illness.

"With thanksgiving. . ."

I once reached into the back of the dryer to pull out a runaway sock and said, "O, Lord, thank You that I can do laundry. . . ." *Wait a minute! What did I just say? I'm thanking God that I can do laundry? I don't want this to be the pinnacle of my life!* But there are many days when I am thankful for the little things, because the day before I could not do them. Thankfulness is a mixed emotion when one has a chronic illness. We're thankful for what we can do; yet we're also angry that life has come down to being thankful about such small successes. We're thankful we're not as bad off as someone else, and then we feel guilty for feeling that way. Our thankfulness scale can become very skewed. But all pain does have a purpose. Walter A. Maier, a preacher in the 1940s who operated twelve hundred radio stations, said, "This is the purpose of pain for the redeemed: it is one of your Father's ways of speaking to you; It is the evidence of His limitless love, by which He would draw you further from evil and closer to Him, the divine remedy that can cure you of pride and help you lean more trustingly on the Lord."[1]

We've been discussing the benefits of having a personal relationship with Jesus Christ, but how does one go about doing so? First, spend time in the Word. "We need— desperately need—the daily cleansing of God's Word, time alone with Him each day, as well as special seasons of deeply searching for His truths."[2] Secondly, I believe it's in accepting the unfathomable gift God chose to give us, His life. Everlasting life is going to be amazing!

In 2 Corinthians 4 the apostle Paul writes about all that we have to look forward to someday. And if we think it sounds good, just wait until we get to heaven; it's better than earthly words can describe! In *Kids Talk About Heaven*, children share some of the highlights they look forward to.

> "My house will be made out of Reese's Cups, and filled with chocolate" says Michael, 6.
> "I think that the streets are gold, the waters are crystal, and the houses are made of clouds," says Kristan, 10. "In God's room, there are TVs so he can see what we're doing all day."
> "The sun always shines there," shares Randy.
> "I want to meet Elvis," Erich, 12, said.[3]

We can barely begin to understand the depth of God's love for us, even when we acknowledge the gift He gave: "God made Him who had no sin to be sin for us, so that in Him we might become the righteousness of God" (2 Corinthians 5:21). Wow! He made Himself sin. . .for you!

A New Perspective

> *"True happiness consists not in the multitude of friends, but in their worth and choice."*
> —*Samuel Johnston*

Paul says, after seeing the gift of life that Jesus forfeited to save us, that from this point forward, "[I will] regard no one from a worldly point of view" (2 Corinthians 5:16). When we crave affirmation and we're disappointed with the lack of sensitivity from the world, it's because we are still looking at the situation from a worldly point of view. We confuse our desires. We think we are simply seeking desires of the flesh from people in the flesh, when what we really desire is affirmation from our heavenly Father that we matter. And we can only get this from our Father. He can even provide the most unique gifts we may have never considered asking for before our illness.

> "What has helped me most is how the Lord has blessed my life. He recently answered a prayer to learn to play the harp as a form of therapy," shares Susan. "A woman generously donated a harp to me, and I found a Christian harp teacher. It is God's blessing in my life. He is there for us and sees our pain and answers our prayers."

As we recognize all that God sacrificed for us — especially His only Son, we can begin to understand Paul's excitement about heaven. He has hope! He witnessed the depth of Jesus' love by seeing His great suffering hanging on that cross so we could be forgiven. Regardless of our circumstances, we always have hope!

Even when it seems we are not physically being healed, God is still at work in our lives. Take, for example, Luke 17:12-19. It tells us a story of Jesus healing ten men who had leprosy. They left, still not healed, but they would be soon. Only one returned to Jesus to thank Him and Jesus asked, "Where are the other nine?" Then He told the man, "Rise and go; your faith has made you well" (Luke 17:19). What He meant was that the man's *thankfulness* had truly made him spiritually well. The others may have been physically healed, but the Samaritan was complete because his heart was transformed as well as his body.

The Temptation of Self-Pity

Robert Schuller says, "It takes but one positive thought, when given a chance to survive and thrive, to overpower an entire army of negative thoughts."[4] Thankfulness can be a challenge if we're comfortable in the victim role or living in a state of self-pity. Proverbs 26:27 says, "If a man digs a pit, he will fall into it." If you believe the world is out to make your life miserable, soon your life *will* be miserable. No rocket science needed. Writer Gerald Sittser says, "Many people are destroyed by loss. . .they choose to wallow in guilt and regret, to become bitter in spirit, or to fall into despair. While nothing they can do will reverse the loss, it is not true that there is nothing they can do to change."[5]

In the Bible it tells the story of Mephibosheth, the son of Jonathan, King David's best friend. When Jonathan was killed, David told Mephibosheth, who was crippled in both feet, "Don't be afraid. . .for I will surely show you kindness for the sake of your father Jonathan. I will restore to you all the land that belonged to your grandfather Saul, and you will always eat at my table" (2 Samuel 9:7). Mephibosheth, "shuffling and stammering, not looking him in the eye, said, 'Who am I that you pay attention to a stray dog like me?'" (v. 8, *The Message*). In the *New International Version* he calls himself a "dead dog." Rather than a spirit of thankfulness, Mephibosheth had a spirit of self-pity and likely suffered from depression. Scriptures seem to emphasize this because he didn't groom himself, even when approaching the king. "He had not taken care of his feet or trimmed his mustache or washed his clothes from the day the king left until the day he returned safely" (2 Samuel 19:24).

Nicki* called me seeking emotional support as well as answers for practical assistance. She desperately needed help in her home with some cleaning and someone to occasionally run errands. "My church offers this kind of thing, but I'd never have them do it," she said.

"Oh, but, Nicki, this is a ministry for them," I said. "Let them help you. It's a gift."

---

* Name has been changed

"I don't need their help. I don't want their pity. I don't want them telling me I need to get out more, or what drugs I should or shouldn't be taking. And my house is just filthy. I'd die before I'd let someone come in and clean. I'm too embarrassed. I'll figure it out somehow."

It is very hard to accept help. I understand. But when we refuse to allow people to minister to us — even if it's just by doing a load of laundry — they will rarely come around

> "Never look at what you have lost; look at what you have left."
> —Robert Schuller

again and offer to help. Are people reaching out to you, and your attitude of self-pity or pride is preventing you from enjoying their gift? Most people love helping others; they just want to feel appreciated and as though they made a positive difference. If they come to clean your house and you act embarrassed, it may come across as a lack of thankfulness and even hostility. We must force ourselves to let go of our pride and say, "You'll never know how much this means to me."

Just this week I received a message from someone named Sharon.* Sharon yelled into the answering machine for the entire two minutes. She declared how unfair life was, how she has no friends, how doctors don't take her seriously, and how her state has zero resources for someone with an illness. Sharon said that my ministry wouldn't likely be able to help her either, and she complained about the greeting on our message machine. She ranted and raved until the machine cut her off. I grieve for Sharon's situation, as I know sometimes it feels like the whole world is out to get you, but I understood why her troubles are seemingly multiplying. She is so furious with the world that friends have deserted her, receptionists likely don't take her seriously, and those who care can do

---

* Name has been changed.

nothing to please her, so they give up trying. She was so upset that I could not understand her phone number to even return her call; but it's doubtful I could have made a difference anyway, because the change will have to begin within her own heart. I sent a prayer upward for her that God would provide what she needs.

Cloud and Townsend speak of this sense of entitlement in their book *Safe People*. Entitlement is a demand for special treatment. Instead of being grateful for ordinary, "good-enough" resources and situations, we demand the best. [For example]:

- Feeling that I deserve a better life than I received.
- A sense that people need to make restitution for their sins against me.
- A need for others to apologize for hurting me before I will get better.
- An inability to feel loved when I am not front and center stage.
- A sense of deprivation when I am not made special to others.
- Feeling that people don't treat me with the respect I deserve.[6]

During the first five years of illness, depression, denial, and especially a sense of entitlement are all a part of the grief cycle, as well as coming to terms with the fact that life may never be the same. Life isn't fair. But we can't take up residence in this state of mind. God doesn't want us to stall here. It's a very lonely, unfulfilling, and "un-fun" way to live!

Thankful for God's Plan

"Having chronic pain for the last twenty years, I have always been searching for relief of some sort. Before finding the Lord—or rather—before He found me, I used illicit drugs, alcohol, and misused medication in numerous ways. With the Lord as my helper, I have found prayer *very* effective in this area. Also, by asking a person to pray for you, you can see his belief system—or lack of one. I recall asking my pastor to pray for me. He looked at me in an incredulous way, as if my chronic pain was beyond prayer! I thank the Lord every day for *never* being beyond my reach and *never* being limited in what He can do!" —Bracy

It can be so tempting to enviously look at those who have earthly comforts. Yet, remember, many of them do not live with any eternal hope. I recently received an email with the signature line that said, "Optimism is the faith that leads to achievement. Nothing can be done without hope." While nonbelievers may appear fulfilled, they are not. We have the hope that purifies us (1 John 3:3). Purifying something is a long, arduous process. Could the Lord have allowed this illness into your life to save you from other conditions which may have been worse? Hezekiah, king of Judah, was healed of an illness, and upon reflecting back he said, "Surely it was for my benefit that I suffered such anguish. In Your love You kept me from the pit of destruction" (Isaiah 38:17). David admits, "It was good for me to be afflicted so that I might learn Your decrees" (Psalm 119:71).

David says to God, "You guide me with Your counsel, and afterward You will take me into glory. Whom have I in heaven but You? And earth has nothing I desire besides You. My flesh and my heart may fail, but God is the strength of my heart and my portion forever" (Psalm 73:24-26). "Wait for the Lord; be strong and take heart and wait for the Lord" (Psalm 27:14). God often delays answering our prayers until we have exhausted all of our resources and talents. Then when He answers our prayers, we must give Him 110 percent credit for the miracle that has occurred. We must hope in God, and this hope "does not disappoint us, because God has poured out His love into our hearts by the Holy Spirit, whom He has given us" (Romans 5:5).

Confusion Is Part of Faith

Paul Billheimer, author of *Don't Waste Your Sorrows*, explains that there is a certain kind of faith we are given that is meant to drive us out of ourselves and into God's arms. Unfortunately, this faith "cannot be developed without being utterly baffled" about God's plan and reasoning. And God may even deny us the feeling of His presence. For example, God seemed so absent during Job's struggles (He was always in control), but God seemed to contradict Himself when He asked Abraham to take the life of his son. All of this is intended to build our character and reveal more about God's character. When our faith is put to the test is when we really choose to rely on our beliefs or on our emotions.[7]

"If you judge people, you have no time to love them."
—Mother Teresa

So perhaps we so much want others to understand simply *because even we* don't fully understand what is going on in our lives. We want someone to validate that our feelings are real and that God still exists even in the darkness. We desperately need relief from all of the confusion encircling us. Sadly, it won't help. There will always be confusion, especially when it has to do with issues of faith and understanding God's will for our lives. Take, for example, Jesus' life. Two thousand years after Jesus' death, scholars still debate the basic facts about His life and death. Throughout the Bible it speaks of the mystery of Christ. This is what defines faith as faith: We believe despite the gaps in the ability to explain the fullness of God's power and love.

We cry out, "How long, O Lord? Will You forget me forever? How long will You hide Your face from me? How long must I wrestle with my thoughts and every day have sorrow in my heart?" (Psalm 13:1-2). Jeremiah was a prophet who poured out his heart to God. His lament to the Lord is about self-pity and his sadness over feeling betrayed. However, then he moves into praises and thanksgiving to the Lord. Read Jeremiah 20 for a wonderful example of inner pain causing outward suffering, and yet leading to a renewed trust in the Lord.

Thankfulness Is an Attitude

Paul writes, "Out of the most severe trial, their overflowing joy and their extreme poverty welled up in rich generosity. For I testify that they gave as much as they were able, and even beyond their ability. Entirely on their own" (2 Corinthians 8:2-3). When it comes to thankfulness, we have no limitations. We can each give as much as we are able, and then lift ourselves up to the Lord so we can continue to pour out our gentleness, mercy, and thankfulness beyond our human ability. The attitude of acceptance that we *can* control our actions is extremely important in the maturing of our faith. Genesis 4:6-7 shows that God has been sending us this message since the beginning of time: "Then the Lord said to Cain, 'Why are you angry? Why is your face downcast? If you do what is right, will you not be accepted? But if you do not do what is right, sin is crouching at your door; it desires to have you, but you must master it." With God's help we can master our sinful nature and let go of emotions that hold us back from (growing into being ([or] becoming) more Christlike.

Billheimer writes, "*It is not always the character of the affliction which determines its spiritual value but rather the length of its continuation and one's reaction to it. Whether the suffering is for and with Christ may be determined not so* much by its nature and severity as by the quality of one's spirit in which is it faced."[8]

We have a unique opportunity to witness to others about God's faithfulness in spite of our circumstances and unanswered prayers. "Joni Eareckson Tada, Christian author and quadriplegic, shares that, when she gets into an elevator with strangers and they are held 'captive,' she sings 'Amazing Grace' until she reaches her floor. She wants to leave people wondering, 'What is it that makes that woman in a wheelchair sing "Amazing Grace?"' Would they be so intrigued if she walked?"[9]

Regardless of what your day may hold, you can always awake with the promise that God already knows "the plans [He has] for you. . .plans to prosper you and not to harm you, plans to give you hope and a future. . . . And your hope will not be cut off" (Jeremiah 29:11; Proverbs 23:18).

Many may question how we can live with chronic illness and still believe in God's faithfulness. I question how anyone can live with illness and not have God beside him or her every day. How do those people make it through the daily pain, without knowing that they have a future and a hope that can never be cut off? Celebrate your Lord. He has overcome the world!

Review

- As we grow closer to the Lord, we lose our worldly perspective and our fleshly desires.
- Though self-pity may be tempting, it leads us to empty and bitter lives.
- God has a plan for your life, and illness won't ever interfere with His promises regarding your future.

Reflection
- How have I experienced thankfulness while living with chronic illness?
- Have I withheld a spirit of thankfulness? Why? Does it feel like "I am giving in to the illness" to be content?
- How has the illness affected my relationships with God? With others?

Scripture
- "Devote yourselves to prayer, being watchful and thankful" (Colossians 4:2).
- "You will be made rich in every way so that you can be generous on every occasion, and through us your generosity will result in thanksgiving to God" (2 Corinthians 9:11).
- "For everything God created is good, and nothing is to be rejected if it is received with thanksgiving" (1 Timothy 4:4).
- "Give thanks to the Lord, for He is good; His love endures forever" (Psalm 118:29).

Action
Make it a habit to write down two things that you are thankful for each morning. Place it on the refrigerator. As a fun family project, have a sheet for each week and have everyone add two things each day. At the end of the year, you'll have a wonderful scrapbook full of memories and thanksgiving.

Prayer
Lord, give me a heart of thankfulness. I surrender over to You the need to understand all the reasons for my illness(es). I surrender over to You all the grief I feel from lost opportunities. I surrender over to You the attitude I sometimes possess that does not bring You glory. I surrender over to You my pain, Lord. You know I desire to

be free from it, but if it's a thorn I must bear, give me the grace and the attitude of thankfulness to bear it with dignity so that it is honoring to You. I don't want to waste a single moment of my suffering. In Your precious name, amen.

Chapter 7

GUARDING OUR
HEARTS AND MINDS
So where do I go from here?

"And the peace of God, which transcends all understanding, will guard your hearts and your minds."

Many of us have felt the sting of a well-intentioned comment that came out all wrong. We've become careful about who we let into our lives, if anyone at all. But to keep our hearts completely protected, we would have to hole up in our home and never open the door or even peek through the curtains. Can you relate with the psalmist who says, "It is better to take refuge in the Lord than to trust in man" (Psalm 118:8)? To expose our hearts and feelings is to risk vulnerability. But is closing our hearts how we are called to live? No, God calls us to open our hearts to Him but also "to one another as Christ has opened His heart to you, and God will be glorified" (Romans 15:7, *New Testament in Modern English*). Opening our hearts isn't all about our own pleasure but also about allowing God to be glorified even if we occasionally get hurt in the process.

Well, I don't close my heart up to God, you might say. *I trust Him. He's safe and He protects me, but I'm tired of being hurt by other people. They just don't get it, and I'd rather just stay at home and pray with my Father than risk going to church and having someone question why I am still using a cane when they prayed for my healing last month.* Just as God desires us to open our hearts, Satan desires us to close them up tightly.

I understand. It's risky! Who of us wants to put ourselves in harm's way? And yet, Satan realizes that by getting us to close off our hearts to others, he is weakening our bond with God Himself. Christ created us in His image, and that includes His heart. Our hearts were designed to be vulnerable, to be open, loving, and gentle. When we say, "Well, I'll open my heart to God but not to people," we are starting down that slippery slope of cutting ourselves off from fellowship, support, love, and our calling to be Christlike. God has called you on a journey of chronic illness. You've likely experienced a few dead ends and a few U-turns. And relationship conflicts could easily be called "potholes." Yet the more intimate relationship we have with our Father, the better we'll be able to roll right over those potholes without getting stuck in them. It's far from biblical, but perhaps Dr. Seuss states it most simply: "Be who you are and say what you feel, because those who mind don't matter and those who matter don't mind." When we stay focused on our identity as Christ's children, we are given a peace that transcends understanding. We're able to be whom God designed us to be without concern about the world's opinion.

> *"The only way to have a friend is to be one."*
> – Ralph Waldo Emerson

Jesus' Friendships Weren't Perfect

Let's look at Jesus' last moments here on earth. Jesus was a risk taker in the friendships He chose. He had only three years to get His ministry off the ground and leave it in the hands of His disciples. Look who He included as disciples: fishermen (did you notice they always seemed to have empty nets?); and even a tax collector who people disliked before he even spoke. Jesus spent three years molding them and modeling God's love for them. They gave up everything to follow Him, and yet Jesus served them just as much. "Rabbi, we need more food! Rabbi, calm the storm!" When your best buddy is the Son of God, wouldn't you be tempted to ask for a few favors? I know after three days of walking dusty, dry roads, I'd be saying, "Lord, can you arrange a Starbucks and a swimming pool out here somewhere?"

Jesus had served them in many ways, even washing their feet from His knees. He finally asked them for a personal favor. He wanted them to stay awake with Him in the Garden of Gethsemane during His last hours. I can only imagine how human Jesus must have been; because, despite His holiness, His very best friends couldn't stay awake for a few hours and keep Him company. If they had truly seen Him as the Son of God without His human qualities, could they have just slipped off into a nap so easily?

Jesus told them, "My soul is overwhelmed with sorrow to the point of death. Stay here and keep watch with Me" (Matthew 26:38). Can you imagine how Jesus must have felt when He returned from His quiet place of prayer and found His best friends zonked out? "Could you men not keep watch with me for one hour?" He asked Peter. "Watch and pray!" (vv. 40–41). Then He went to pray again. Did He pray, "God, are You sure about letting Me leave them here on their own? Do You think they are ready to be Your ambassadors?" Is there any doubt that *God* saves the world, not us?

Jesus came back after praying the second time. Were the disciples awakening, preparing to fix an early morning campfire breakfast of eggs and biscuits? The coffee was on, right? Hardly! It was still dark and, not surprisingly, for the second time they were sound asleep. I can't help but hear them snoring away as Jesus walks up and rolls his eyes, and turns back around to go and pray a third time. He arrives back at the garden. His heart is very heavy about what His Father is requiring of Him today, as it is the day He will be given his death sentence, even though He has never committed a single sin. With His friends all snoozing in the garden during His *third* prayer, however, I can't help but believe He felt disappointed. "Oh, Father, have I taught them anything? They can't even stay awake! They have so many challenges and battles in store for them. Will they ever make it, when they can't even do Me this one simple favor? I really needed to feel their love. I needed to know they cared and were here for Me. Thank You, Father, for being enough for Me, for being My full portion."

Joni Eareckson Tada explains in *When God Weeps*, "It's poignant that when the Son of Man walked on earth he had the comfort of his Father, but none from his friends. No fellowship of suffering on this planet for him. He only had the blind insensitivity of His disciples. No moral support. No joy in carrying his cross—he bore it 'for the joy that was set before him.' He went without comfort so that you might be comforted. He went without joy so that you might have it. He willingly chose isolation so that you and I might never be alone. Most wonderfully, he bore God's wrath so that you wouldn't."[1] We'll never find that perfect friend anywhere else than at the foot of the cross.

When Others Want a Miracle

So we must guard our hearts wisely but not turn our hearts off. We must fellowship with others but worship only the Lord. One area in which I've seen some hearts broken is the conflict of emotions that arise when our friends want to see us healed. They want a miracle. This is an area we need to take to the Lord, so that He can give us the peace that transcends all understanding.

When Jesus spoke, large crowds would come from miles around to hear Him speak. There is no doubt, however, that a large percentage of them came to see the miracles that He performed and the people that He healed. Our human desire to see miracles is not much different today. When we have a chronic illness, we may be surrounded by those who want to pray for our healing. Whether it is the elders of the church or the neighbors who arrive at your doorstep, everyone wants to be a part of seeing God work in wondrous ways.

> *"It is said that in some countries trees will grow, but will bear no fruit because there is no winter there."*
> —*John Bunyan*

We are not to worship the miracles but God Himself. Even Jesus became frustrated with the "groupies" who only showed up to see Him perform the miracles. "I did one miracle, and you are all astonished" (John 7:21). Over and over Jesus healed people and told them "go and don't tell anyone of your healing" (see Matthew 8:4). He wasn't looking to be the local magician and create a circus. He merely wanted to stand and teach about His Father. To reduce God's holiness to a trick was an insult; yet because of His compassion, it was as though He couldn't turn a single person away. He "heal[ed] every disease and sickness among the people" (Matthew 4:23b).

Today, when a healing doesn't occur, people offer advice or slowly drift away. It's difficult for them to accept that God said no when they are sure they followed the Bible's instructions on "praying properly."

"My adult daughter has said on more than one occasion, 'You really should be healed by now! When you pray for healing are you believing you'll be healed?'" shares Cheryl, who lives with various chronic conditions. "She means well but she just doesn't understand."

Many Christians believe it must be something within us. Either we have sin in our lives or we do not have enough faith. Regardless, when we are not healed, it's natural that a certain amount of our friends will become less interested when the fireworks show doesn't take place.

Suffering Is Part of God's Will

Regrettably, we must acknowledge that suffering is part of God's will. "In fact, everyone who wants to live a godly life in Christ Jesus will be persecuted" (2 Timothy 3:12). We can cling to God's promise: "I have told you these things, so that in Me you may have peace. In this world you will have trouble. But take heart! I have overcome the world" (John 16:33). But suffering is a deep theological issue many do not agree on.[i] We can be confronted by friends who believe that we must not really want to be well if we're not willing to at least try their advice. "What can it hurt?" they ask.

> "I had a friend call and ask me if I was setting goals for myself," shares Liz. "Evidently, she read an article about lupus, and I had just confided in her about what a terrible time I am going through. This really hit me wrong. Most people who are ill are motivated people who set goals and don't need people to tell them. When you are sick it is so easy to beat yourself up and feel that you are not doing enough. Advice makes it worse. I desperately need support and reassurance that I am doing the best I can."

I was cornered at a pre-crusade dinner by a well-meaning woman who knew everything there was to know about treating illness with herbal remedies because she had a "friend of a friend who went to a guy" who had furnished some good results for someone. She followed me around

---

[i] An excellent book on this topic is *When God Weeps* by Joni Eareckson Tada.

the buffet line trying to convince me that I should go see "this guy." Have you ever met someone who had all the answers and she knew God had sent her into your life to "instant message" them to you? "The man who thinks he knows something does not yet know as he ought to know" (1 Corinthians 8:2). In other words, the wisest people are those who admit they have few answers, especially when it comes to understanding suffering. Paul Billheimer, author of *Don't Waste Your Sorrows,* writes, "Evidently God has objectives in us which cannot be achieved apart from frustration and bewildering pain.... This was the way Job's faith was perfected so that he said, 'Though he slay me, yet will I trust in him" (Job 13:15 [KJV]).[2]

This kind of God who expects us to suffer, however, is not easily understood, nor is suffering for His sake valued by our society. "It is difficult to find anyone in our culture who will respect us when we suffer," writes Eugene Peterson in his book *A Long Obedience in the Same Direction.* "We live in a time when everyone's goal is to be perpetually healthy and constantly happy and if any one of us fails to live up to the standards that are advertised as normative, we are labeled as a problem to be solved, and a host of well-intentioned people rush to try out various cures on us. Or we are looked on as an enigma to be unraveled in which case we are subjected to endless discussions in which our lives are examined by zealous researchers for the clue that will account for our lack of health or happiness."[3] You may find it interesting that this book was written in 1980. Not much has changed in our quest for health and healing.

Let's look at some situations that may occur in our lives and how to best respond to them, guarding our hearts and minds, but with a peaceful resolution.

When Others Are Eager for Your Healing

Be cautious about adopting zeal for *healing* instead of zeal for *God's will*. According to Billheimer, "Suffering is not only the last thing to be considered useful, but rather something to be avoided, evaded, and shunned. But, according to the Word of God, suffering is not an accident but a gift to be cherished, for when properly received it works to enhance one's eternal rank, fame, and honor."[4] Despite the fact that we believe all illness does have a purpose, it's very hard for those who love us, however, to see good in any of our pain.

Read with me the apostle Paul's comments to the Galatians about his illness: "As you know, it was because of an illness that I first preached the gospel to you. Even though my illness was a trial to you, you did not treat me with contempt or scorn. Instead, you welcomed me as if I were an angel of God, as if I were Christ Jesus Himself. . . . It is fine to be zealous, provided the purpose is good" (Galatians 4:13–14, 18a).

A pastor recently asked me what the best way was to share "medical breakthroughs" with one who has an illness. I told him there was no one way that would always produce a positive result, but before taking any action to ask himself the following:

- Am I doing it for my own glory—to look good, smart, caring, and concerned? Do I just want to be a part of a miracle and have some role in a healing? Is this something that seriously could be helpful or just the latest news he is probably already aware of?
- Or am I doing it because I genuinely care and want the other person to feel better, but I acknowledge that God is the One who is always in control?

He laughed and sheepishly said, "I've done it for both reasons." I said, "So have I." Test your own motives when you reach out to others. Are your motives zealous for the right reasons?

People may also wish to anoint you with oil, as described in James 5. This is a biblical practice that is still alive in many churches today. However, many ill people feel pushed into being anointed. Note that James 5:14 says, "Is any one of *you* sick? *He* should call the elders of the church to pray over him and anoint him with oil in the name of the Lord." In other words, it is the responsibility of the sick person to ask for prayer and anointing. Right after the diagnosis of my illness, my church held an "anointing service," and I felt highly pressured to attend, but I resisted. I was questioned by many, "What can it hurt? Why not just try it? You need to have faith and believe you will be healed!" So why didn't I go? Simply because I didn't feel God calling me to go. I felt His assurance and peace that surpassed the understanding of what seemed logical to everyone else. God said, "Not yet," and I felt that when it was time He would tell me. Thankfully, I did not attend a church where I was forced into this situation, as I know many people are.

There is also one more point worth noting: verse 15 of James, chapter 5. In the NIV it says, "And the prayer offered in faith will *make the sick person well*; the Lord will raise him up." This makes it sound like one is guaranteed a healing if everything in James 5 is completed without error. However, this is a misinterpretation. In the King James Version it says, "And the prayer of faith *shall save the sick,* and the Lord shall raise him up." Douglass Connelly, author of *How Can I Pray When I'm Sick?* says, "The prayer of faith is, after all, a prayer, and like all prayer it stresses our willingness to rest on the wisdom and provision of God. When the prayer of faith is given by God, it accomplishes his purpose, and whether immediately or gradually, the sick one gets better."[5] We will all "get better" when we enter the kingdom of God. People who believe we are always healed here on earth have yet to explain why the death rate is 100 percent. Make sure your focus is on God's will for your life regardless of what He chooses to do with it, instead of waiting until you are healed to begin to live.

When Someone Says Words That Hurt

> "I am a pastor's wife. At our previous church, I was repeatedly judged by church members because my house (their pastorium) wasn't clean, that I didn't curl my hair, or wear enough makeup, or that I wasn't supporting my husband's ministry when I wasn't there (even though I could prove through church records that I was there more than 'the complainer.') People even accused me of making up my illnesses. I'm worse physically than I've ever been before, but our new church has supported my husband and me more. The Lord knew I would need this church at this time, and I praise Him for it. " —Donna

When someone says words that hurt, guard your heart by acknowledging that you only have so much control over the situation, and then do your best to resolve it, responding with grace. Those around us watch us to see how we—as believers—will respond to an unjustified "attack," such as rude comments. If we respond no differently than nonbelievers, how have we represented God? Romans 12:17–18 says, "Be careful to do what is right in the eyes of everybody. If it is possible, *as far as it depends on you*, live at peace with everyone." By choosing to do your best, as far as it depends on you, you are refusing to play the victim role, but rather taking initiative in using this as a growth opportunity. When you choose the victim role of "Why are *You* doing this to *me*?" your spiritual growth becomes stagnant. Remember, "The Lord is close to the brokenhearted and saves those who are crushed in spirit" (Psalm 34:18). Don't miss out on an unexpected blessing by turning away from God or seeking revenge because of your pain.

How to Respond When Someone Wrongs You

"During my most difficult years with fibromyalgia, I had fatigue beyond measure and had a hard time keeping up on my housework, but my house was always presentable when I had company. But during our church leadership meetings at my home, the women would make comments on how they would've cleaned the candle holder better than I did, or they wouldn't drink out of the glasses in which I offered them a drink (which had been run through the dishwasher and were perfectly clean)." —Stacy

When our hearts are broken we naturally want to hurt the person back, but we must surrender this desire over to the Lord. Then our hearts do not become hardened. God will still deal with the other

> *"My flesh and my heart may fail, but God is the strength of my heart and my portion forever."*
> —*Psalm 73:26*

person—but in His manner, which is always more effective than our own. The Bible tells us, "Do not repay anyone evil for evil. . . . Do not take revenge, my friends, but leave room for God's wrath, for it is written: 'It is mine to avenge; I will repay,' says the Lord. On the contrary: 'If your enemy is hungry, feed him; if he is thirsty, give him something to drink. In doing this, you will heap burning coals on his head.' Do not be overcome by evil, but overcome evil with good" (Romans 12:17, 19–21).

Respond to the one who has hurt you with a peaceful, calm heart. You will represent a God who gives mercy. Ironically, God doesn't just let one off the hook; He creates a turmoil of emotions within the other person. When someone feels angry and guilty, and you respond with kindness, it can feel like burning coals on her head, because she is dealing with shame over her own actions. Not fun!

Pray for the One Who Hurt You — with Compassion

It may take time to get to this point, but "be diligent in these matters; give yourself wholly to them, so that everyone may see your progress" (1 Timothy 4:15). Ask the Lord to work in your friend's life and to soften your heart toward him or her. Ephesians 4:2 says, "Be completely humble and gentle; be patient, bearing with one another in love."

Pray to Forgive the One Who Hurt You

Even if the one who has hurt you has moved on, passed away, or desires no relationship with you, ask for God to provide forgiveness in your own heart so you can let it go and have more intimacy with the Lord. "For if you forgive men when they sin against you, your heavenly Father will also forgive you. But if you do not forgive men their sins, your Father will not forgive your sins" (Matthew 6:14–15). Kind of blunt, isn't it? God knows we need to forgive in order to be fully His.

In the book *Answers to Satisfy the Soul*, author Jim Denney defines forgiveness as "a choice to renounce the anger or resentment against an offender." He says that forgiveness is a decision we make, not an emotion we feel. Feelings such as anger and resentment will come and go. "But," he says, "if we make a *decision*, we can *will* ourselves to abide by that decision, despite our wavering feelings. . . . We can't simply press a 'delete' button on our memories. In fact, our brains are constructed in such a way that the most painful memories tend to be the ones that are the most permanently imprinted. So forgetting is *not* a component of forgiving. Fact is, we must forgive precisely because it's *impossible* to forget. The memory of the hurt will come back to us again and again, so we must make a deliberate choice to renounce anger and resentment."[6]

Test Your Own Actions

We often assume that those around us have not experienced chronic illness (after all, they look so good!). John 7:24 warns us, however, "Stop judging by mere appearances, and make a right judgment." Sometimes we are the first ones to assume someone is illegally taking our disabled parking spot because they look normal. When we do this, we must realize how natural it is to flip to the other side and begin judging people on their appearances instead of facts. Think of others before yourself. The other day, a driver cut me off in traffic and then zoomed through the grocery store parking lot. I commented to my husband, "Maybe she has a sick child at home who needs some medicine fast." What are the odds of this? Who knows? But when we automatically assume there are reasonable explanations for one's actions, rather than malicious intent, we don't take their actions personally, even when they inconvenience or exasperate us.

Test your actions without comparing, "I wasn't nearly as cruel as my friend was!" Honestly ask yourself, "How could I have made the situation worse? Could my actions have been misinterpreted? What would I do differently if I could do it again?" Galatians 6:4 says, "Each one should test his own actions. Then he can take pride in himself, without comparing himself to somebody else." Ask God for forgiveness. Ask Him to convict you of your wrongdoings so you can ask for forgiveness of the individuals and of the Lord. Helen Keller once said,

"Character cannot be developed in ease and quiet. Only through experience of trial and suffering can the soul be strengthened, ambition inspired, and success achieved."

Learn How to Set Healthy Boundaries

> *"There are vast, untapped resources of faith that can be discovered only in adversity."*
> —*Robert Schuller*

Proverbs 12:26 tells us that "a righteous man is cautious in friendship." If you've been deeply hurt by someone, it may be time to set new boundaries. These may be resented, so be careful that when you do set boundaries, to "not let any unwholesome talk come out of your mouths, but only what is helpful for building others up according to their needs, that it may benefit those who listen" (Ephesians 4:29). Use "I" language: "I will be able to come for one hour, but then I will have to leave." "I love you but I don't want to discuss the topic of ___ with you. Is there something else we can talk about?" "I appreciate you sharing your feelings with me, but I won't be able to accommodate your requests." Regardless of the response you receive, "Get rid of all bitterness, rage and anger, brawling and slander, along with every form of malice. Be kind and compassionate to one another, forgiving each other, just as in Christ God forgave you" (Ephesians 4:31–32).

Ask God for a Trustworthy Friend as You Reach Out to Others

When we've been hurt by people, isolation may seem like a reasonable protective measure to take; but isolation is, in fact, very dangerous.

> "Envy, self-sufficiency, entitlement, and transgressions push us further into isolation," says Cloud and Townsend. "The result of that isolation is generally some sort of breakdown.

Like a car running out of gas, we stop functioning well. We act out our addictions, get depressed, and function poorly in relationships. However, these 'bad deeds' are only a symptom of the deeper problem: the *disconnection* caused by envy, self-sufficiency, entitlement, and transgressions."[7]

It's very important that you have a special travel companion on this journey of chronic illness. Don't hold back in asking God to bring people into your life to help you cope and be encouraged, as well as ones you can encourage. Henri Nouwen, author of *Out of Solitude*, says, "When we honestly ask ourselves which person in our lives means the most to us, we often find that it is those who, instead of giving much advice, solutions, cures, have chosen rather to share our pain and touch our wounds with a gentle and tender hand. The friend who can be silent with us in a moment of despair or confusion, who can stay with us in an hour of grief and bereavement, who can tolerate not knowing, not curing, not healing, and face us with the reality of our powerlessness, that is a friend who cares."[8]

We miss out on an amazing part of life when we don't create relationships. Don't be afraid to take steps toward seeking them out. Cloud and Townsend offer their advice:

"Warning: passivity is hazardous to your health. If you're passive, you may find that it's hard to reach out and take initiative in relationships. You may wait by the phone, hoping someone will call. . . . There's nothing wrong with desiring these kinds of encounters. But remember that you'll need to do your part too. 'And if he shrinks back, I will not be pleased with him' (Hebrews 10:38)."[9]

Too often, when we are the ones who do not feel well, we sit back and wait for someone to encourage us. But when you live with illness, you may be isolated and not easily available to invitations. Instead, you will have to take the initiative to make a phone call, send an encouraging card, tell someone you prayed for them, or even do your grocery shopping with a friend. Many people love to feel needed, and your invitation to someone to go get a haircut together or buy your grandchild a present may not be an intrusion at all, but rather a welcome invitation.

We are told to guard our hearts and minds; however, we must do this with wisdom and discernment from the Lord, being cautious not to close off our hearts and minds completely. It is through the peace of God that our hearts and minds will be guarded. Make sure the Lord is the One who is protecting your heart and that it's not your own fears that are preventing you from forming relationships. Fellowship and friendship are a part of our well-being that God designed for us to experience.

Review
- We'll never find the perfect friend on this earth. If we're unhappy with our relationships, it may be because our expectations are too high or because we're choosing the wrong people to form friendships with.
- Although it's normal for people to want you to be miraculously healed, suffering is part of becoming more like Jesus. It's easy to get caught up in worshipping what Jesus could do for us rather than who He is.
- We must allow God to be in control and surrender our hurt feelings and human social desires over to Him.

Reflection
- How have I closed myself off from relationships, based on poor past experiences? Or how have I been tempted

to do so but have pursued forgiveness instead? What was it that made me do this?

- How much does it affect me when people want me to be healed? Am I passive and allow them to do and say whatever they want? Am I understanding and polite, but set healthy boundaries? Or do I come off as resentful or inconsiderate to others' desire to see me well?
- How can I continue to build solid friendships through my lifetime, despite my illness? How might my illness have a positive impact on my relationships?

Scripture
- "Devote yourselves to prayer, being watchful and thankful" (Colossians 4:2).
- "See to it that no one takes you captive through hollow and deceptive philosophy, which depends on human tradition and the basic principles of this world rather than on Christ" (Colossians 2:8).
- "This is what the Lord says: 'Cursed is the one who trusts in man, who depends on flesh for his strength and whose heart turns away from the Lord,'" (Jeremiah 17:5).

Action
Step out of your comfort zone and pursue getting to know someone better. Call your church and see if there is someone who may need to be encouraged. Call someone who has been on your mind lately just to let them know you're thinking of them. If you need help, decide to call and invite someone on an outing that could be beneficial to both of you.

Prayer
Lord, I acknowledge that people are not perfect. I will likely get my feelings hurt many times during this lifetime.

Help me recognize that these comments have nothing to do with Your truths and that You are the only One I need to please. I ask for Your strength in offering grace and forgiveness to those who hurt me. And for compassion and wise words when I respond or offer comfort to others. Provide me with discernment in knowing how to set healthy boundaries, learning to say no, standing up for myself, all while reflecting Your love and character. In Jesus' holy name, amen.

Chapter 8

IN CHRIST JESUS
Fulfilling my purpose by reaching out to others

"In Christ Jesus. . ."

> "I have not had a lot of understanding and support at home; my depression got so severe that I decided to take my own life. I ended up in a psych unit, and it was at this point I realized I wasn't alone; and I had Someone who did understand—God. He let me live for a reason. He guided me to take a course from the Arthritis Foundation on teaching self-help courses, and now I head up the support group here at work. God is always there and I never feel hopeless and alone anymore." -Patty

Psalm 68:6 says, "God sets the lonely in families." What does becoming part of God's family mean exactly? How are we "in Christ Jesus"? How do we put what we've learned into practice "in Christ Jesus"? I believe that as Christians who live with chronic illness, we are thrown into a special refinement process; it's painful, but God has hand-chosen those of us who will use our illnesses to glorify Him, even more than He could have used our health. We learn an extraordinary amount about God's character, and we are personally invited to share in His sufferings.

Uh. . .excuse me, you may ask. *Did you just say "share in His sufferings?" Ick! Can I return my invitation?* Sorry, but no. Your illness will forever change you and your relationship with Christ and those around you, for the better—or the worse; your choice. Attitude has a large impact on what will become of this lesson the Lord is offering us.

Adjusting Our Attitude

Let's look at Jesus' attitudes for example: He didn't take things personally. People said a great deal of hurtful things to Him, but He knew that they didn't know who God was. Even at the time of His death, He said, "Father, forgive them, for they do not know what they are doing" (Luke 23:34). He refused to argue with people. He recognized that some people just wanted to cause problems, not genuinely find answers to their questions. Others, such as the Pharisees, tried to make Jesus look foolish or contradictory. In Mark 8:12-13, after the Pharisees questioned Him, He sighed deeply, made a brief statement, refused to argue, and then just left. He recognized that their minds were made up and even He—the Son of the Creator—couldn't change their minds because they had free will.

> *"Life need not be easy to be joyful. Joy is not the absence of trouble but the presence of Christ."*
> —*William Vander Hoven*

Imagine! If Jesus couldn't change the minds of men, why do we believe we have this power within ourselves?

Regardless of what people said to Jesus, He concentrated on His mission and God's purpose for His life. Maturity is realizing that the world does not revolve around us and that every action or reaction is not personally directed toward us. It frees us to become who God wants us to be without concern for what people think. We are focused on who we are in Christ Jesus, not who we are in someone's opinion.

When you turn your illness over to God, you allow God to work through it and use it to His advantage. When you fight God about your illness and all the unfairness that comes along with it (which is a natural response), He'll understand; He'll love you anyway, but eventually you'll probably turn it over to God if you want to find peace within the pain. God has a way of teaching us the same lesson over and over until we eventually learn it. We were even forewarned, "Do not be surprised at the painful trial you are suffering, as though something strange were happening to you" (1 Peter 4:12).

Many people feel, "God gave me this illness." Others take great offense at this viewpoint and claim that illness is the result of living in a sinful world and God simply allowed it. Personally, I look to Luke 14:27: "Anyone who does not carry his cross and follow Me cannot be My disciple." My illness is a cross that I choose to accept to carry. Regardless of what you believe, join me in clinging to Romans 11:36: "For from Him and through Him and to Him are all things. To Him be the glory forever! Amen." Whatever the reason for this cross we are asked to carry, God was involved in the decision-making process 100 percent. But you are responsible for making sure that it glorifies God. Imagine for a moment a large cross sitting in your backyard leaning up against the house. Go on out there with a wood-burning kit and burn in the name of your illness. This is your cross. It may be temporary or it may be permanent, but you can choose to throw tar and feathers at it or get out some decoupage and see what God is going to make out of it. By carrying your cross, you are a disciple. Welcome to the family.

We Were Designed to Love One Another

Robert Schuller says, "We learn courage when we face danger. We learn patience when we endure suffering. We learn tenderness when we face pain."[1] Did you know that one of the reasons we are called to suffer is so that we can comfort others? "Whatever you have learned or received or heard from me, or seen in me—put it into practice. And the God of peace will be with you" (Philippians 4:9). Now that we're experiencing God's work in our lives, we're called to put what we've learned into practice and provide tenderness to those who are hurting. Have you been fulfilling this calling that you've been given?

It's easy to become busy and caught up in our own lives, but then there is no fruit produced, or as Paul writes, "Nothing good lives in me. . ." (Romans 7:18). Many of us are not taking advantage of reaching out to others, using the unique experiences that God has given to us. We were designed to be interdependent and encourage others. David felt this need: "But when I was silent and still, not even saying anything good, my anguish *increased*" (Psalm 39:2). Wait! Read that verse again. Simply avoiding sin *doesn't* reduce your anxiety. If you aren't doing something positive, your anxiety will still *increase*! I'm not sure about you, but I don't need my worries increasing any—even a little!

Your ministry doesn't have to be an organized, formal chronic illness ministry. Your outreach could be any kind of empathy you would have offered as a Christian, even before your illness. However, now that you've experienced pain and know the significant difference it makes when someone cares, you may be more likely to reach out. "Empathy leads to action," say Cloud and Townsend in *Safe People*. "When you see the pain of another, you want to help. God created you that way. We spend time listening to a friend's struggle not because that will make her like us, but because she needs to be understood. We help someone with a problem not so that we'll feel better, but because she is in trouble."[2]

This is one of my favorite Scriptures: "Praise be to the God and Father of our Lord Jesus Christ, the Father of compassion and the God of all comfort, who comforts us in all our troubles, so that we can comfort those in any trouble with the comfort we ourselves have received from God. For just as the sufferings of Christ flow over into our lives, so also through Christ our comfort overflows. If we are distressed, it is for your comfort and salvation; if we are comforted, it is for your comfort, which produces in you patient endurance of the same sufferings we suffer. And our hope for you is firm, because we know that just as you share in our sufferings, so also you share in our comfort" (2 Corinthians 1:3-7).

Imagine a flower garden filled with people you are to comfort with God's Holy Spirit. God is the spout and you are the garden hose. God's love and comfort flows through you to water the precious lives in that garden. No matter how tightly you are connected to the water spout of the Lord, eventually, if you don't do some watering, you're going to burst and detach from the spout. The spout was never meant to work effectively with a hose that had the end closed off. When we just keep soaking God up without passing Him on, life becomes clogged up and our relationship with God suffers.

> *"The person who tries to live alone will not succeed as a human being. His heart withers if it does not answer another heart. His mind shrinks away if he hears only the echoes of his own thoughts and finds no other inspiration."*
> —*Pearl S. Buck*

Having Patience

While we are told that "each of us should please his neighbor for his good, to build him up" (Romans 15:2), we are also reminded that there will be those who will not understand our predicament. "We who are strong ought to bear with the failings of the weak and not to please ourselves" (Romans 15:1). When I am confronted by a person who believes healing is always given to us by

completing a formula of do's and don'ts, I feel saddened
for him. Because at some point in his life, God will not
work exactly as he has predicted. At some time, God won't
answer his prayers the way he expects. When his faith is in
the formulas instead of in God's mysterious and free will,
his world will shatter. Bear with those who have not yet
experienced a refinement process by the Lord. They do not
yet understand the wondrous ways that He works within
painful circumstances, as you are discovering. Accepting
this is the first step toward loving them. "When we learn
to accept people who disappoint us by no longer requiring
them to satisfy us, then we're free to love them, to reach
toward them for their sake without having to protect
ourselves from feeling disappointed by their response to
us. [3]

We Don't Have Any Excuses

I never enjoyed physical education class in school. I looked
forward to the times when I would have a written note
from my mom excusing me from participating because of
something like a recent illness. It's easy to fall into treating
the commandments of the Bible like a P.E. class. *Well, I'm
excused from that because I have an illness.* For example, I've
seen many people refuse to *be* a friend to someone in need
because they are too self-involved about who is or is not
being *their* friend or caregiver.

My church hasn't even realized I'm not attending. . . .
  The pastor hasn't brought me Communion in six months. . . .
    The only time I ever got a meal was when my husband died. . . .
    I keep getting "get well" cards. I'm not going to get well!
    How am I supposed to "get involved" when I'm ill?

All of these are valid statements; however, our illness does
not exempt us from God's instructions to reach out to

others. In fact, it requires more of us: Luke 12:48 says, "From everyone who has been given much, much will be demanded; and from the one who has been entrusted with much, much more will be asked." Yes, you have been given much, because it is through adversity we come to know the Lord most intimately. Your testimony is stronger after you've been through the fire of refinement. . .and now you must share what God has done for you. We're called to action! "Dear children, let us not love with words or tongue but with actions and in truth" (1 John 3:18). Renee Bondi said in an interview with *HopeKeepers Magazine*:

> *"Life need not be easy to be joyful. Joy is not the absence of trouble but the presence of Christ."*— change already on p118 —*William Vander Hoven*

"I think [church outreach to the disabled] is something we as disabled people should take on. We ask ourselves, 'What do I have to offer to society?' and this is a *huge* job — to come to our pastor or parish advisory board and say, 'What are we doing *really* to minister to the disabled? Can I help? Can I start a Bible study for the disabled? Can I make sure we have an accessible church? If I'm disabled, how can I sit with my family?' It's absolutely important not to go in with a hardened heart and with an attitude of, 'You owe it to me, you're my church!' But rather offer yourself to be part of the solution. Don't be an angry, bitter, demanding person."[4]

Action!

Building Others Up

People aren't perfect. . .and because we know the Lord personally, we are responsible for acting the way He would expect us to. "And the Lord's servant must not quarrel; instead, he must be kind to everyone, able to teach, not resentful. Those who oppose him he must gently instruct, in the hope that God will grant them repentance leading them to a knowledge of the truth" (2 Timothy 2:24–25). As Christians who have experienced at least part of the refinement process, hopefully, we have become more mature in our faith. By forcing others to understand us, we aren't trying to build others up; we are trying to please ourselves. But love is not self-seeking. We've personally experienced the healing power of words and actions, and now we're called to give them, not just receive them.

Know Where Your Worth Comes From

If you're feeling discouraged, here is a healthy reminder that your worth never comes from what you can do, but from who you are. You are so precious to your Savior. There are hundreds of Scriptures that describe all you are to the Lord. Here is a sampling.

Chosen, holy to Him, treasured possessions	*Deuteronomy 7:6*
God's workmanship, planned in advance	*Ephesians 2:10*
Benefactors of God's inheritance	*Deuteronomy 18:2*
Children of God through faith in Christ Jesus	*Galatians 3:26*
The light of the world	*Matthew 5:14*
Forgiven	*1 John 1:9*
God's heirs	*Romans 8:17*
Predestined to be adopted	*Ephesians 1:5*

The Joy in Comforting Others

We are called to be a comforter for others, to reflect His love. Harold G. Koenig, author of *Spirituality in Patient Care: Why, How, When, and What* says, "People who provide support to others are better off themselves and they even live longer."[5] If you don't have any desire to offer comfort to others, it may be because you are seeking your own comfort from other people and coming up empty! We're unable to give to others what we ourselves have not yet received, and we can only receive it from our Lord.

> "My faith in Jesus has taught me how to live in a more positive way," shares Judy, who lives with polycystic kidney disease and breast cancer, among other illnesses. "Now God is putting people in my path. My sister was diagnosed with breast cancer and has to have chemo, and I've been sending her Rest Ministries' devotionals and have been her guide through her difficult days."

Don't feel like you need to have all the answers in order to comfort people. It's your own experience and vulnerability that will make you credible and trustworthy to people. Larry Crabb says, "Everything in spiritual community is reversed from the world's order. It is our weakness, not our competence that moves others; our sorrows, not our blessings that break down the barriers of fear and shame that keep us apart; our admitted failures, not our paraded successes that bind us together in hope."[6] For this journey of chronic illness, most of us would prefer to take along a travel companion who has "been there" rather than a travel agent who has just "heard about" chronic illness. Your experience will be a great blessing to others who are lost and overwhelmed on this unplanned trip!

"Several folks at church have invisible illness, and when I ask these folks how they are doing after they say the usual, 'I'm fine.' I respond by saying, 'Now tell me how you are *really* doing. This shows them that I really am interested in how they are. Another thing I tell the ones I know better is, 'You look like crud. . . .' It's a sort of private joke between us, but it acknowledges the fact that I realize they are not having a good day, and we can talk if they need to. Most of the time it just brightens their day by giving them a good laugh." —Theresa

Take a moment to look closely at 2 Corinthians 1:3-7, on how God has planned in advance for His people to be comforters. . .and what's required of them.

"Praise be to the God and Father of our Lord Jesus Christ, the Father of compassion and the God of all comfort,	*Notice, we begin by rejoicing!*
"Who comforts us in all our troubles,	*Not just some of the troubles but all of them. Even when we can't feel His comforting hand, He is there.*
"So that we can comfort those in *any* trouble	*We're not just talking illness here but any discomforts.*
"With the comfort we ourselves have received from God.	*We've received a gift and now we're accountable to God. Have you used your gift?*
"For just as the sufferings of Christ flow over into our lives,	*Yes, we will suffer. . .*

"So also through Christ our comfort overflows.	*...but we'll also be overwhelmed with how Christ will comfort us in the midst of the suffering.*
"If we are distressed, it is for your comfort and salvation;	*Our suffering always has a purpose.*
"If we are comforted, it is for your comfort, which produces in you patient endurance of the same sufferings we suffer.	*Our sufferings will build character, patience, and compassion for others who suffer.*
"And our hope for you is firm, because we know that just as you share in our sufferings, so also you share in our comfort."	*We always have hope that God is always with us. He shares in our sufferings, but also our comforts; and because we know this to be true, we can share in the sufferings of others. True friends share both the good and bad times.*

It does take effort to be a good friend, but it's often the little things that make the most difference to someone who is hurting. It takes one's presence — not presents! Hugs, not handshakes. "And do not forget to do good and to share with others, for such sacrifices God is pleased" (Hebrews 13:16). God does recognize that doing good and sharing with others is not always convenient, nor are we always in the right frame of mind; but it's still expected of us, and He recognizes it as a sacrifice that we will be rewarded for.

"A friend whose illnesses are much more debilitating than mine told me when I was diagnosed that she was here for me to talk to and to share experiences. She listened when I complained at first, although I know that had to take great forbearance on her part. She's offered great practical advice with organizing my house so it is easier for me to function without stooping or lifting. I thank God for her ministry to me." —Lenore

I love how Lenore describes her friend's actions as "her ministry to me." This is how we can all be "doing ministry." Remember that the people who come to you and share their strong opinions or thoughtless comments are not seeking to intentionally hurt you; they themselves are hurting and searching to find their own meaning in life. They are afraid of their own vulnerability to illness. The world gives them no shortage of stories to make themselves appear noble, but these stories come from a sense of insecurity and false pride. Recognize that those who say things that hurt may be the most in need of your comfort.

The Grace of Friendship

Many friendships form over shared tears as well as the laughs. Friendships can become our lifeline or our main source of discouragement. It often depends on what we are searching for.

Let's face it! We're hurting! While our friends are pursuing wonderful careers, we are sitting in waiting rooms with people thirty years older than us, who look at us with pity. While friends splurge on vacations, we're trying to figure out where the next mortgage payment will come from, or how we will pay for a needed surgery that insurance refuses to cover. We have lots of reasons to expect people to reach out to *us*. Like the friends in the movie *Notting Hill,* we may subconsciously play the game "who has the saddest life," competing to win, if not their sympathy, at least the last brownie.

When you give grace generously and willingly it will be returned, sometimes not by that specific person, but by the Lord. "And God is able to make all grace abound to you, so that in all things at all times, having all that you need, you will abound in every good work" (2 Corinthians 9:8). What powerful words. We will have *all* that we need at all times through God. When we open our hearts, He makes grace *abound* to us and then we pass this on.

Oftentimes, our experiences and our willingness to just be present and available is a ministry unto itself. "Suffering tempers our easy optimism and checks our prejudices. You can often recognize those who have suffered. They are slow to give opinions when some issue is being discussed. They are patient with those caught in some sin. They withhold judgment because they have felt its sting."[7]

"One lady who suffers greatly with back pain had quit coming to our church services completely. When she heard I was starting a HopeKeepers class at our church, she and her husband have been faithful in attendance. She is a real inspiration to all of us in the class. She comes in each Sunday with her walker, bent over to where she mostly looks at the floor. . .but she has good comments in class, and always has a smile and hug for others. She has been a blessing to me! I see her coming into class, and I think, *Lord, this is why You made me able to come this morning when I thought I just couldn't!*" —Alice

Like Alice's experience, our best response is not what comes out of our mouths but out of our hearts. Sometimes just our showing up makes a difference in someone's life.

> *"On the mountaintop we are overwhelmed by God's presence. In the wilderness we are overwhelmed by His absence. Both places should bring us to our knees; the one, in utter awe; the other, in utter dependence."*
> *— Dave Dravecky*

I remember barely making it to church one day, and staying in the painful chair simply because my legs had swollen while sitting and would not straighten easily. Leaving would have caused too much of a disruption. When the final worship song began, I winced and eased them into place, gradually standing, using my husband to try to balance, as the fluid in my legs adjusted. I was discouraged. God knew how hard it was for me to sit there, and yet the sermon had left me empty, not full of the encouragement I so needed. About two weeks later a woman from church, Kathy, approached me after the service and told me she had chronic fatigue syndrome. "A couple of weeks ago I barely made it here; I was in so much pain," she said. "I felt so frustrated and alone. And then I saw you a few rows ahead of me trying to stand and I thought, *She understands! Someone here understands!* It made all the difference to me." I had no idea Kathy had a chronic illness, and I was very humbled. When I had selfishly thought, *God, You didn't give me what I needed!* God had simply used my illness to encourage another person. All I'd had to do was show up.

The apostle Paul encourages us, "Whatever happens, conduct yourselves in a manner worthy of the gospel of Christ. . .without being frightened in any way by those who oppose you. This is a sign to them that they will be destroyed, but that you will be saved—and that by God. For it has been granted to you on behalf of Christ not only to believe on Him, but also to suffer for Him" (Philippians 1:27–29). Simply put, you don't have to fix it all; encourage others without being intimidated by those who oppose you. And conduct yourself so people will see Jesus in you — even when you are suffering.

Moving Forward

So, what now? It is my prayer that this book has made you stop and think more deeply about how much God cares about you. He desires a relationship with you where all your needs are fulfilled through Him. I hope this book has added perspective to the emotions you may experience when you swing your car into a "blue space" or someone asks you why you aren't healed. I hope the *Reflection* questions provide you with a means to think more deeply and that the Scriptures offer you a new kind of peace. Take comfort that none of us is perfect.

I hope this book has brought a new kind of understanding about some of the confusing emotions that accompany living with a chronic illness. Don't focus on your sins, however, and allow guilt and shame to enter into your life. Ask for forgiveness and move forward. John Ortberg, author of *Love Beyond Reason*, says, "God sees with utter clarity who we are. He is undeceived as to our warts and wickedness. But when God looks at us that is not all he sees. He also sees who we are intended to be, who we will one day become."[8] God doesn't see you with a chronic illness. He sees your spirit, your heart, and the glow of His glory within you. He sees your character developing to be more like His own. He sees you as one He loves and longs to comfort.

Psalm 62:1–2, 8 says, "My soul finds rest in God alone; my salvation comes from Him. He alone is my rock and my salvation; He is my fortress, I will never be shaken. . . . Trust in Him at all times, O people; pour out your hearts to

Him, for God is our refuge." Ray Pritchard, author of *Keep Believing*, says, "Be encouraged, child of God. He loves you even in the midst of your pain. He loves you even when you don't love Him. He loves you when you feel utterly alone. He loves you with an everlasting love. Your suffering can take many things away from you — your health, your happiness, your prosperity, your popularity, your friends, your career, even your family. But there's one thing suffering can't take away: It can't take away the love of God."[9]

God's Word is powerful, and I urge you to get out your Bible and see just how applicable it is to your everyday life and situations. And when you study it, God will reveal many new things to you! Things you will never read about in books such as this. "You have heard these things; look at them all. Will you not admit them? From now on I will tell you of new things, of hidden things unknown to you" (Isaiah 48:6). It's vital that we pay attention to God's response to the people written about in the Bible, such as when the Israelites complained or Moses became arrogant: "For everything that was written in the past was written to teach us, so that through endurance and the encouragement of the Scriptures we might have hope" (Romans 15:4). "These things happened to them as examples and were written down as warnings for us, on whom the fulfillment of the ages has come" (1 Corinthians 10:11).

There is great joy and hope that can always be found at Jesus' feet that cannot be found in a relationship with anyone else. He created us to need Him, to thirst for Him, to have our quench fulfilled only by Him. When I read the following passage in *Don't Waste Your Suffering*, it expressed words of hope from God the Father that I wanted to share with you.

"Are you passing through a night of sorrow? This thing is from Me. I am the 'Man of sorrows and acquainted with grief.' I have let earthly comforters fail you, that by turning to Me you may obtain everlasting consolation (2 Thess. 2:16–17). Have you longed to do some great work for Me and instead been laid aside on a bed of pain and weakness? This thing is from Me. I could not get your attention in your busy days and I want to teach you some of My deepest lessons. 'They also serve who only stand and wait.' Some of My greatest workers are those shut out from active service, that they may learn to wield the weapon of all prayer.

"This day I place in your hand this pot of holy oil. Make use of it freely, My child. Let every circumstance that arises, every word that pains you, every interruption that would make you impatient, every revelation of your weakness be anointed with it. The sting will go as you learn to see *Me* in all things."[10]

Why can't I make people understand? you may ask. Because... there is no need. God understands, and He is all you will ever need. Let go of the desire for others to understand.... "Because of the Lord's great love we are not consumed, for His compassions never fail. They are new every morning; great is Your faithfulness. I say to myself, 'The Lord is my portion; therefore I will wait for Him" (Lamentations 3:22–24).

Review
- Our attitude about our illness is significant in how God uses it and how our faith grows.
- We were designed to bring comfort to others, but we can only do this if we receive comfort from our Father.
- Just because we have a chronic illness doesn't mean we're exempt from reaching out to others; in fact, we're more called to do so.
- Friendships will never be perfect but loaded with grace.
- God is all we will ever need.

Reflection

- How is my attitude about my illness? Have I viewed it as a thorn from the Enemy or as a chisel of God? How might an attitude adjustment change my everyday outlook?
- Have I used my illness as an opportunity to reach out to others who are hurting, or as an excuse not to form friendships, since people don't understand?
- What are some ways I can tangibly reach out to others? What are the challenges I'll need to overcome in order to do this?
- How can I use what I've learned in this book to change my life in order to allow God in deeper and let others' opinions slide off of me?

Scripture

- "'Love the Lord your God with all your heart and with all your soul and with all your mind and with all your strength.' The second is this: 'Love your neighbor as yourself.' There is no commandment greater than these," (Mark 12:30–31).
- "Show proper respect to everyone: Love the brotherhood of believers, fear God, honor the king" (1 Peter 2:17).
- "I tell you the truth, anyone who has faith in Me will do what I have been doing. He will do even greater things than these, because I am going to the Father" (John 14:12).
- "Yet the Lord longs to be gracious to you; he rises to show you compassion. For the Lord is a God of justice. Blessed are all who wait for Him!" (Isaiah 30:18).

Prayer

O, Lord, I ask for Your guidance as I seek to use the gift You've given to me within my illness. It's so easy to think of ways in which I am not being served by others, yet instead I should be rejoicing for all that You provide me with and passing along Your comfort to others. Your Word tells me, "Who can discern his errors? Forgive my hidden faults" (Psalm 19:12). Lord, I ask for forgiveness for the hidden faults I have that I do not realize. Help me learn what they are so I can work on these areas of my life. Provide me with mentors, friends, and opportunities to show the world just all that You have done for me throughout my suffering and within my suffering. In Jesus' precious and holy name, amen.

NOTES

INTRODUCTION
1. Lisa Copen, "Carrie Carter: When the Doctor Becomes Ill" *HopeKeepers Magazine,* Vol. 1, Issue 2 (San Diego, CA: Rest Ministries), Jan/Feb 2004, p. 9.
2. Larry Crabb, *Inside Out* (Colorado Spring, CO: NavPress,1998), p. 73.
3. Max Lucado, *Just Like Jesus* (Dallas, TX: W Publishing, 2003), p. 3.

CHAPTER 1: Rejoicing in God
1. *Webster's Revised Unabridged Dictionary,* © 1996, 1998 MICRA, Inc.
2. Carole Mayhall, *Words That Hurt, Words That Heal* (Colorado Springs, CO: NavPress, 1989), pp. 106–7.

CHAPTER 2: Being Gentle
1. Larry Crabb, *Inside Out* (Colorado Springs, CO: NavPress, 1998), p. 74.
2. Cheri Register, *The Chronic Illness Experience* (Center City, MN: Hazelden Information Education, 1999), pp. 60–61.
3. Henry Cloud and John Townsend, *Safe People* (Grand Rapids, MI: Zondervan, 1995), p. 58.
4. (author,article?), *HopeKeepers Magazine,* Vol. 1, Issue 2 (San Diego, CA: Rest Ministries), Jan/Feb 2004. page?
5. Carole Mayhall, *Words That Hurt, Words That Heal* (Colorado Springs, CO: NavPress, 1989), pp. 106–7.
6. Cheri Register, *The Chronic Illness Experience,* (Center City, MN: Hazelden, 1999), p. 69.
7. Larry Crabb, *Inside Out* (Colorado Springs, CO: NavPress, 1998), p. 74.
8. Henry Cloud and John Townsend, *Safe People* (Grand Rapids, MI: Zondervan, 1995), p. 81.
9. Ibid., p. 75.
10. Cheri Register, *The Chronic Illness Experience,* (Center City, MN: Hazelden, 1999), p. 102.
11. Sheila Cragg, *A Woman's Pilgrimage of Faith: A Daily Guide for Prayer and Spiritual Maturity,* (cityState?: Crossway Books, 1999), p. 85.

CHAPTER 3: Acknowledging God's Presence
1. Stormie Omartin, *Just Enough Light for the Step I'm On* (Eugene, OR: Harvest House, 1999), pp. 42–43.
2. Robert Schuller, *Little Book of Hope* (Nashville, TN: Thomas Nelson, 1996).
3. Oswald Chambers, *My Utmost for His Highest: An Updated Edition in Today's Language* (Grand Rapids, MI: Discovery House, 1992), May 11.
4. Larry Crabb, *Inside Out* (Colorado Springs, CO: NavPress, 1998), p. 41.

CHAPTER 4: Letting Go of Anxiety

1. Larry Crabb, *Inside Out* (Colorado Springs, CO: NavPress, 1998), p. 92.
2. Ibid., p. 93.
3. Pat Williams and Jim Denney, *How to Be Like Jesus: Lessons on Following in His Steps* (Deerfield Beach, FL: Faith Communications, 2003), p. 69.

CHAPTER 5: Praying and Petitioning

1. James MacDonald, *Lord, Change My Attitude (Before It's Too Late!)* (Chicago, IL: Moody, 2001), p. 37.

Pat Williams and Jim Denney, *How to Be Like Jesus: Lessons on Following in His Steps* (Deerfield Beach, FL: Faith Communications, 2003), p. 241, John R. Cogdell quoted, electronics engineer and educator.

Christine M. Anderson, compiler. *Stories of Comfort for a Healthy Soul* (Grand Rapids, MI: Inspirio/Zondervan, 2001), p. 70.

4. James MacDonald, *Lord, Change My Attitude (Before It's Too Late!)* (Chicago, IL: Moody, 2001). p 147.
5. Larry Crabb, *Inside Out* (Colorado Spring, CO: NavPress, 1998), p. 149.
6. Ibid., see p. 151.
7. Douglas Connelly, *How Can I Pray When I'm Sick?* (Downers Grove, IL: InterVarsity, 1999), pp. 8–10.
8. Larry Crabb, *Inside Out* (Colorado Spring, CO: NavPress, 1998), p. 153.
9. Mark Cosgrove, *Counseling for Anger* (Nashville, TN: W. Publishing, 1988). p. 81.

CHAPTER 6: Giving Thanks

1. Christian Quote Database.
2. Carole Mayhall, *Words That Hurt, Words That Heal* (Colorado Springs, CO: NavPress, 1989), p. 40.
3. Eric Marshall, *Kids Talk About Heaven*, (New York, NY: Crown, 2003).
4. Robert Schuller, *Little Book of Hope* (Nashville, TN: Thomas Nelson, 1996).
5. Gerald Sittser, *A Grace Disguised: How the Soul Grows Through Loss* (Grand Rapids, MI: Zondervan, 1998) p. 87.
6. Henry Cloud and John Townsend, *Safe People* (Grand Rapids, MI: Zondervan, 1995), p. 86.
7. Paul E. Billheimer, *Don't Waste Your Sorrows* (Minneapolis MN: Bethany House, 1983), pp. 51–52.
8. Ibid., p. 59.
9. Lisa Copen, *Mosaic Moments* (San Diego, CA: Rest Ministries, 2002), p. 20.

CHAPTER 7: Guarding Our Hearts and Minds

1. Joni Eareckson Tada, *When God Weeps* (Grand Rapids, MI: Zondervan, 2000), p. 143.

CHAPTER 8: In Christ Jesus

1. Robert Schuller, *Little Book of Hope* (Nashville, TN: Thomas Nelson, 1996).
2. Henry Cloud and John Townsend, *Safe People* (Grand Rapids, MI: Zondervan, 1995), p. 45.
3. Larry Crabb, *Inside Out* (Colorado Springs, CO: NavPress, 1998), p. 117.
4. Lisa Copen, "Renee Bondi" *HopeKeepers Magazine,* Vol. 1, Issue 2, (San Diego, CA: Rest Ministries), Jan/Feb 2004, p. 11.
5. As quoted in Bob Holmes, Kurt Kleiner, Kate Douglas, and Michael Bond, "Reasons to be Cheerful" *New Scientist*, Vol. 180, Issue 2415 (4 October 2003), p. 44.
6. Larry Crabb, *The Safest Place on Earth* (Nashville, TN: W Publishing, 1999), p 32.

[7] Gordon Houser, Christian quote database.

[8] John Ortberg, *Love Beyond Reason* (Grand Rapids, MI: Zondervan, 2001), p. 24.

[9] Ray Pritchard, Calvary Memorial Church, sermon on 6/27/1993. Series: *New Life In Christ* (Romans 5–8), www.calvarymemorial.com.

[10] Paul E. Billheimer, *Don't Waste Your Sorrows* (Minneapolis MN: Bethany House, 1983), p. 66.

NATIONAL INVISIBLE CHRONIC ILLNESS AWARENESS WEEK

Did you know nearly 1 in 2 people in the USA live with a chronic condition? And 96 percent of the illnesses are invisible!

National Invisible Chronic Illness Awareness Week, held annually in September, is a designated time worldwide, in which people who live with chronic illness, those who love them, and organizations are encouraged to educate the general public, churches, health-care professionals, and government officials about the effects of living with a disease that is not visually apparent.

For more information visit www.invisibleillnessweek.com or contact Rest Ministries, the sponsor of this week at 858-486-4685.

ABOUT THE AUTHOR

Lisa Copen founded *Rest Ministries, Inc.*, in 1997 after four years of living with a chronic illness (rheumatoid arthritis). Although she has found that God's plan for her life is much different than she expected, she intends to share her experiences in order to comfort others. She is a popular author and speaker, especially among the chronically ill community and beyond.

Lisa is the author of a variety of books including *Mosaic Moments: Devotionals for the Chronically Ill; Why Can't I Make People Understand?; When Chronic Illness Enters Your Life* and *Learning to Live with Chronic Illness* (bible studies), *How to Start a Chronic Illness Small Group Ministry;* and *A Woman's Health Record-Keeping Journal.* She lives in San Diego, California with her husband, Joel, and son, Joshua. You can reach her through the web site at www.restministries.com.

ABOUT REST MINISTRIES

Rest Ministries, Inc. is a nonprofit Christian organization that exists to serve people who live with chronic illness or pain, and their families, by providing spiritual, emotional, relational, and practical support through a variety of resources, including Bible studies, and small group materials. The ministry is an affiliate ministry of Joni and Friends, the ministry outreach of author and speaker, Joni Eareckson Tada.

Rest Ministries also seeks to bring an awareness and a change in action throughout churches in the USA, in regard to how people who live with chronic illness or pain are served, and teach churches effective ministry tools in ministering to this population.

Designed with your specific needs in mind, *RestMinistries.com* will encourage you on your Christian walk while you live with chronic illness and pain.

- Articles about the things that matter to you: feelings, friends, family, finances, and faith
- Daily devotionals from others who live with chronic pain.
- Alternative medicine — biblical perspectives of when it helps and when it hurts
- Peer advice about living with chronic illness and growing in your faith
- Book excerpts and book reviews to help you on this journey
- Interviews with celebrities and hidden heroes
- Updates on HopeKeepers Groups and how to start a HopeKeepers ministry
- A social networks with a variety of ways to meet others, including groups for men, moms, those coping with depression, hobby-related, Bible studies online and more.